PENGUIN CANADA

Family Quizmas

GORDON PAPE is the author of many acclaimed books, including bestselling investment guides, novels, and non-fiction humor. He is the father of three and grandfather of eight, and has spent many Christmases playing *Quizmas* with friends and family.

DEBORAH KERBEL, Gordon's daughter, is a seasoned *Quizmas* player and mother of a young son and daughter. She is the author of *Kendra's Chronicles.*

The authors live in the Toronto area.

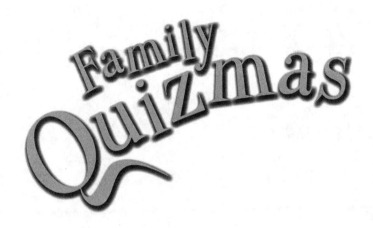

Family Quizmas

Christmas Bedtime Stories & Trivia Fun

Gordon Pape and Deborah Kerbel

PENGUIN
CANADA

PENGUIN CANADA

Published by the Penguin Group

Penguin Group (Canada), 90 Eglinton Avenue East, Suite 700, Toronto, Ontario, Canada M4P 2Y3
    (a division of Pearson Canada Inc.)

Penguin Group (USA) Inc., 375 Hudson Street, New York, New York 10014, U.S.A.
Penguin Books Ltd, 80 Strand, London WC2R 0RL, England
Penguin Ireland, 25 St Stephen's Green, Dublin 2, Ireland (a division of Penguin Books Ltd)
Penguin Group (Australia), 250 Camberwell Road, Camberwell, Victoria 3124, Australia
    (a division of Pearson Australia Group Pty Ltd)
Penguin Books India Pvt Ltd, 11 Community Centre, Panchsheel Park, New Delhi – 110 017, India
Penguin Group (NZ), cnr Airborne and Rosedale Roads, Albany, Auckland 1310, New Zealand
    (a division of Pearson New Zealand Ltd)
Penguin Books (South Africa) (Pty) Ltd, 24 Sturdee Avenue, Rosebank, Johannesburg 2196, South Africa

Penguin Books Ltd, Registered Offices: 80 Strand, London WC2R 0RL, England

First published 2006

(WEB) 10 9 8 7 6 5 4 3 2 1

*Publisher's note: This book is a work of fiction. Names, characters, places and incidents
either are the product of the author's imagination or are used fictitiously, and any
resemblance to actual persons living or dead, events, or locales is entirely coincidental.*

Manufactured in Canada.

LIBRARY AND ARCHIVES CANADA CATALOGUING IN PUBLICATION

Pape, Gordon, 1936–

Family quizmas : Christmas bedtime stories and trivia fun / Gordon Pape ;
Deborah Kerbel, contributing author.

ISBN-13: 978-0-14-305544-0
ISBN-10: 0-14-305544-5

1. Christmas--Miscellanea. I. Kerbel, Deborah II. Title.

GT4985.P33 2006   394.2663   C2006-902808-7

Visit the Penguin Group (Canada) website at **www.penguin.ca**

Special and corporate bulk purchase rates available; please see
www.penguin.ca/corporatesales or call 1-800-399-6858, ext. 477 or 474

Dedication

To Xenya, Abby, Jonah, and Dahlia:
May all your Christmas memories be joyous

Contents

Introduction

*T*he stories of Christmas are among the most beautiful in the rich heritage that has been passed down to us over the millennia. We have all heard them many times over the years, and yet they are always new and exciting.

We wrote this book to introduce the wonder of Christmas to the youngest of children, to help them better understand the enchantment, the mystery, and the true meaning of this most special day.

As parents, we know from experience that many of the great Christmas stories are difficult for very young children to understand, and some, such as the Dickens classic *A Christmas Carol,* are simply not suitable for small children. So we set out to retell the greatest of these stories in a way that will fascinate and enthrall even the youngest girl or boy. Seven traditional stories are included in this book, one for each night of the week leading up to Christmas Eve.

We begin each story with a Quizmas question, so the child is immediately involved in the tale to come. At the end, we have added two more questions your child can have fun answering before drifting off to sleep. If he or she wants more—and we know some youngsters love answering questions like this—we've added another seventy, ten for each story, at the end of the book.

Here's a little background to the stories and how we decided on the best ways to retell them.

THE NATIVITY STORY. Only two of the Gospels tell the story of the Nativity: St. Matthew and St. Luke. Our version draws heavily on St. Luke, which describes most of the events we have come to associate with the story of Jesus' birth. We have added some description and characters to the biblical story, so as to make it more interesting to young children. For example, the innkeeper's wife is not mentioned in the scriptures, although scholars agree that Mary almost certainly would have had at least one woman in attendance at the birth, as was customary at that time. But apart from these minor changes, the story we tell is the same as it appears in St. Luke.

THE THREE KINGS. Here we found ourselves dealing with a different situation. The story of the Three Kings appears only in St. Matthew and is very sketchy. Many people are surprised to learn that St. Matthew does not even tell us how many kings there were—some scholars say there could have been as many as twelve. In fact, it is not even clear that "kings" is the correct way to describe them. The word *magi*, as used in the original Greek (the language in which the Gospels were written), can be interpreted as "wise men," as it is in the King James Version of the Bible. The Three Kings have also been described over the centuries as "magicians" or "wizards."

There is no mention in St. Matthew of their names or where they came from. Balthasar, Melchior, and Gaspar, the names most widely accepted today, come from accounts written years later, and there was no unanimity even then that they were correct. It is widely agreed, however, that the Three Kings came from different places and met only when they reached Jerusalem. In Psalm 72, verse ten, we read that "the kings of Tarshish and of the isles shall bring presents: the kings of Sheba and Seba shall offer gifts." From that verse, latter-day scholars and artists concluded that Ethiopia, Arabia, and Tarsus, on the south coast of what is now Turkey, were the homelands of the Three Kings.

St. Matthew also offers clues that suggest the Three Kings did not visit the Christ Child at the stable in Bethlehem, as tradition-ally depicted, but in fact arrived about two years after his birth. In chapter two of this Gospel, we are told that King Herod sent the Wise Men to Bethlehem, following the star. But verse nine refers to Jesus as "the young child" (King James Version). Further on, in verse eleven, Matthew writes, "And when they were come into the house, they saw the young child with Mary his mother." These words suggest that the Holy Family was living in a permanent residence, not a stable. We are then told that an outraged Herod ordered the killing of all the children under age two in Bethlehem "and in all the coasts thereof." Some have interpreted these passages as indicating that Joseph and Mary lived in Bethlehem following the birth of Jesus and remained there for two years, until an angel told them to flee to Egypt after the visit of the Three Kings.

Because St. Matthew's account is so brief and is open to interpretation, we have based much of our retelling of the Three Kings on legend, scholarly accounts, and a large dose of imagination. However, we believe we have been true to the original premise of the story and that your child's understanding of the meaning of gift-giving will be enhanced by it.

THE CHRISTMAS ANIMALS. St. Matthew's version of the Nativity makes no mention of animals, and the only reference in St. Luke is to the flocks the shepherds were watching. However, over the centuries many stories and legends have evolved about the roles various animals played in the birth of Jesus.

The most common is the depiction of Mary riding to Bethlehem on a donkey. It is logical to assume she would have ridden, given that she was close to giving birth and so walking such a distance would have been very difficult, perhaps impossible, for her. She could have been seated on a horse or even a camel, but the donkey (or the ass, as it is commonly referred to in old stories) seems an appropriate choice in light of the Holy Family's humble circumstances. For that reason, we chose to make the donkey the main character in our story.

The other references in the story are based on well-established legends, including the robin fanning the fire and burning its breast, the ox warming the Baby Jesus with its breath, the stork's feathers lining the manger, and the cock crowing from the roof to proclaim the birth of the Christ Child. In fact, in Spanish-speaking countries, Midnight Mass is sometimes referred to as the *Misa del Gallo* ("Mass of the Rooster"). According to some folk tales, the nightingale sang "Gloria in excelsis deo" along with a choir of angels over the sleeping Jesus.

The buzzing bees story is a curious one. According to Irish legend, all the bees in the world hum Psalm 100 in unison on Christmas Eve. This is the psalm that begins "Make a joyful noise unto the Lord, all ye lands. Serve the Lord with gladness: come before his presence with singing." It is said that only the pure of heart can hear this wonderful sound.

The belief that animals can speak in human voices at midnight on Christmas Eve was fairly widespread in medieval Europe and persists to this day in parts of Scandinavia, where children stay up late to hear the animals rather than watch for Santa. But some stories claim it is bad luck to hear the animals speak, so if your children decide they want to try, perhaps you can discourage them by telling them this.

A CHRISTMAS CAROL. We regard *A Christmas Carol* as one of the most finely crafted stories in the English language. Charles Dickens's classic tale of greed and redemption speaks to all of us, and as writers we approached his work with the greatest respect.

However, in its original form, *A Christmas Carol* is not suitable for small children. To begin with, it is too long—it would take at least a couple of hours to read it through. Equally important, the language, beautiful as it is, is too dense for a young child to understand.

We wanted to tell the story in a way that would appeal to Deborah's three-year-old son, Jonah, who became our first focus group of one. We set out to rework it by retaining the key characters, the most important events, and the underlying message of the story without unduly frightening or, perhaps worse, boring a child. Based on Jonah's reaction (he loved the character of Marley's ghost) and that of other children who listened to it later, we believe we succeeded.

THE NUTCRACKER. We're all familiar with this tale as a fanciful ballet performed every year at Christmastime, but most people don't realize that the ballet is derived from a much more intricate story called *The Nutcracker and the Mouse King,* written by German composer and writer Ernst Theodor Amadeus (E.T.A.) Hoffmann. Hoffmann, better known in Europe than in North America, was a great storyteller and the inspiration for Jacques Offenbach's celebrated opera *The Tales of Hoffmann.*

In 1816 Hoffmann wrote a whimsical, somewhat weird, and sometimes gory children's book about a young man who is bewitched by the spell of a vengeful mouse and turned into a nutcracker. Now, two centuries later, we thought it would be wonderful to dust off and resurrect the original story, which has been overshadowed by the famous ballet. With great respect to Hoffmann, we felt, however, that it needed some reworking to make it suitable for a younger audience. The result, we hope, will become a new favorite in your child's Christmas storytime collection.

THE STORY OF ST. NICHOLAS. We've all heard Santa Claus referred to as St. Nick, but many of us are unfamiliar with the real St. Nicholas, who, back in the fourth century, was a bishop in what is now the southern coast of Turkey. Arguably one of the most popular of the saints, his feast day on December 6 is widely celebrated in Europe.

St. Nicholas is well loved by many people. In fact, he's the national saint of Russia and Greece and the patron saint of barrel makers, thieves, sailors, judges, murderers, pawnbrokers, merchants, paupers, scholars, bakers, maidens, and poor children—a highly diverse group, to say the least. But, because of his reputation for generosity to and fondness for children, he has always been closely associated with Christmas.

We thought your children would be interested in hearing some of the legends surrounding this holy man who became the inspiration for our modern-day Santa Claus. Two stories in particular are well known within the church, one of which we felt was too gruesome to tell in this book since it involves the murder of three boys and their restoration to life by the saint.

The other story inspired the tradition of the Christmas stocking. Using a bit of poetic license, we've retold it here in the hopes that our young readers might come to know the true spirit of generosity that is at the heart of good old St. Nick.

A JOURNEY TO SANTA'S CASTLE. To end the book, we wanted to create a fun little story about how a child might imagine Santa's castle. And so we set our grown-up imaginations loose for a while, and what they came back with was pure fantasy: snowmen sentries, stocking-repair rooms, a team of tired reindeer asleep on red velvet beds, and a Santa Claus who smells like a candy cane.

With a dash of folklore and a generous helping of whimsy added in, we thought this was just the kind of story our young audience would want to hear before going to sleep on Christmas Eve. We hope you, and they, agree!

As we adapted these stories, we had before us the vision of a loving parent or grandparent sitting by the bedside, reading to a young child who listens in rapt attention as shepherds kneel before the manger, as the Three Kings traverse great distances with their gifts, as animals help to warm the Baby Jesus, as Scrooge learns the true meaning of Christmas, as St. Nicholas performs his miraculous deeds, and more. We hope our vision will come true in many homes around the world.

Christmas has been a part of our family forever. We love everything about it, and we want our children and grandchildren to share in the wonderful memories we have stored away over the years. Through this book, we hope to share our feelings for this special time with others—with you, our grown-up reader, but most especially with the youngsters in your life.

So please enjoy watching the light in your children's eyes as you read these marvelous stories to them. And a merry Christmas to all!

Share Your Christmas Memories

*W*e all have our own family memories of Christmas. This is a special invitation to share them with others. We have created a website at www.quizmas.net where we devote a special section to memories our readers have sent to us. Some of the stories are very moving, some are humorous, others tell of unusual traditions, and a few offer genuine surprises.

Take some time during the holiday season to visit the website. We guarantee you'll enjoy the experience. And when you have finished reading the reminiscences, send us your story—anything you think would bring joy or fun or hope or faith to others. It may be a favorite Christmas recipe, a childhood memory, or a life-changing Christmas event. If it is special to you, it will be special to others as well.

We'll post the best ones on Quizmas.net, and perhaps we can put together a book of Christmas nostalgia that the world can enjoy.

To participate, go to www.quizmas.net and use the email Christmas Memory form you'll find there. Or write to

Suite 181
16715 – 12 Yonge Street
Newmarket, Ontario
Canada   L3X 1X4

Please try to keep your items to fewer than 1,000 words.

Don't be shy. Christmas is about giving, and among the most valuable things we can give to anyone are good memories, because when we're gone, so are they.

The Nativity Story

Tonight we're going to read the first story from a book that's all about Christmas. Do you think you'd like that? This story is about the first Christmas ever. Before we start, let's see if you can answer a question about that day.

Your Quizmas Question

Whose birthday do we celebrate on Christmas?
Is it the birthday of Santa Claus?
Is it Jack Frost's birthday?
Is it your birthday?
Is it the birthday of the Baby Jesus?

What do you think? Let's turn the page for the answer.

Your Quizmas Answer

Did you say the Baby Jesus? You're right!
Although no one is sure of the exact date of the
Christ Child's birth, over the years people in most
parts of the world have celebrated it on December 25.
That's Christmas Day.
Do you know the wonderful story of the night
Jesus was born? Let's read it together now.

*H*undreds and hundreds of years ago, in a land far away, a young man named Joseph and Mary, his wife, were traveling along a valley road as nightfall approached. He walked, while she rode on a small donkey that carefully picked its way along the muddy track. Their new baby was due to be born any day now.

Mary was tired and sore. Riding a donkey isn't very comfortable and it had been a long day. Now, as they approached the little town of Bethlehem, she felt something stirring inside her.

"Joseph!" she called to her husband, who was leading the donkey. "We must find somewhere to stay. I think the baby is coming."

But all the houses were dark and closed up against the cold winter drizzle that fell from the sky. There was not a friendly light to be seen.

Joseph looked around at the dark streets, unsure which way to turn. It had been many years since he had been in Bethlehem.

"I think there is an inn up ahead, at the town square," he said after a few moments. "I'm sure they will have room for us."

Mary shivered and wrapped her cape more tightly around herself.

"There! Just ahead!" Joseph cried as they turned a corner.

Sure enough, flickering torches welcomed travelers to a cozy inn. They could hear voices coming from inside.

Joseph quickened his pace and urged the donkey forward. Soon they were at the door.

"I'll find the innkeeper," he said, tying the donkey's lead to a post. "We'll have you warm and snug in no time."

But a few minutes later he returned, his face downcast.

"They're full," he said sadly. "There is nothing for us."

"Then we will go elsewhere," Mary replied.

"There is nowhere else to go. The innkeeper says that every place in town is full."

"But what are we to do?" Mary asked. She felt another stirring inside and knew they had little time.

Joseph said sadly, "I don't know."

At that moment, the innkeeper appeared at the door. He was a large man with a big belly and a friendly face.

"I've been talking to my wife," he told them. "We agreed that we can't just send you away, not on a night like tonight and with a baby coming. There is a stable behind the inn where you can stay if you want. It's not much, and you will have to share it with the animals. But at least you will be out of the rain, and the straw is warm and dry."

"Thank you so much," said Mary. "I'm sure it will do just fine." The innkeeper felt the whole square light up with her smile.

"We'll send out some food for you," the innkeeper said, as he turned to go back inside. "You must be starving."

Joseph untied the donkey and led them to the stable. Inside it was as the innkeeper had said: small and humble, with an assortment of cows, donkeys, goats, and chickens. But the room was warm and the hay was dry and welcoming. A cow mooed softly as Joseph helped Mary down and led her to a quiet corner, where he set up a bed of straw for her.

A few minutes later, the innkeeper's wife appeared with a basket of fruit and sweet-smelling, freshly baked bread. When she saw that Mary was about to give birth, she fussed over her, helping to make her comfortable and speaking softly to her.

"I must go back and help my husband," she said when she was sure Mary was settled in. "The water from the pump over there is good to drink. If you need anything at all, please come for me," she said to Joseph.

With that, she left them alone.

Now, Mary and Joseph knew that the baby she carried was no ordinary child. Months before, when they were living in the town of Nazareth, the angel Gabriel had appeared to Mary in a dream to tell her of God's plan.

"God will send you a Son and you will name him Jesus," the angel had said. "He will be the Son of God and he will reign over the world forever."

Gabriel then told Joseph how Mary was to be blessed. So when they arrived in Bethlehem, they both knew that something very special was about to happen.

And so it came about in the small hours of the night. As the town slept, Mary quietly gave birth to a beautiful baby boy. It happened so easily that she needed no help, and when she held the baby in her arms she marveled at how peaceful he was, for he never once gave out a cry.

The heat from the animals helped to keep the stable warm, but to protect the Baby Jesus from the night chill, Mary wrapped him tightly in swaddling clothes and laid him on a bed of straw in a manger. Then, while the animals looked on, she and Joseph knelt to give thanks to God for the lovely child.

In winter, the hills of Judea, where Bethlehem is located, can be cold and damp. But shepherds must watch over their flocks of sheep in all weather. So it was that as Mary was giving birth in the town below, a small group of shepherds huddled around a fire, trying to keep warm and to get a little sleep.

Suddenly, a strange thing happened. The entire hillside was bathed in light, as if the sun had unexpectedly risen in the middle of the night. The shepherds were frightened and their sheep bleated nervously.

"What's happening?" cried a young boy, who had been awakened by the brightness.

"I don't know," said an older man, his knees trembling. "I don't know, I don't know." He looked as if he were about to run away.

And then they heard a strong yet gentle voice.

"Fear not," it said. "I bring you good tidings of great joy, which shall be to all people."

They looked up and saw a shining angel hovering above them. The light that had awakened them seemed to come from within his body, and he was smiling down on them.

The angel continued. "A great miracle has taken place tonight in Bethlehem. A Savior has been born to the blessed Mary and he is Christ the Lord."

"A Savior?" one shepherd asked.

"Christ the Lord?" said another.

"Where?" asked a third.

The angel spoke again.

"You will find him in the stable behind the inn at the town

square. He will be wrapped in swaddling clothes and lying in a manger."

"A manger?"

"Our Lord?"

"How can that be?"

The shepherds were confused and uncertain. As they waited for an answer, the sky was suddenly filled with a host of singing angels, whose voices echoed across the hills.

"Glory to God in the highest," they sang. "And on earth, peace, good will toward men."

And then, just as quickly, they were gone and the sky was dark again.

The shepherds stared at one another in the dim light from the fading fire.

"Was that a dream?" one asked.

"Did it really happen?" wondered another.

"How can such things be?" questioned a third.

Then the little boy spoke up.

"How will we know, unless we go and see for ourselves? Follow me. I know a short path to the town."

And so the group of humble shepherds followed the path down the hill, entered Bethlehem, and made their way to the stable. When Joseph came to see what they wanted, they told him the story of the angel who had told them to come see the baby for themselves.

Joseph returned to the manger and spoke softly to Mary for a moment. She nodded, and he motioned to the shepherds to enter.

They shuffled in, awed at the scene before them, whispering to one another so as not to disturb the sleeping Jesus. They had never seen anything like this. Usually, a stable is filled with the sounds of braying donkeys, bleating goats, clucking chickens, and mooing cattle, but on this night it was silent. The animals stood quietly, as if they too were aware that something had taken place that had never happened before.

The shepherds stood around the manger, then fell to their knees in prayer. They stayed there for what seemed a very long time. Then, silently, they rose and went out into the night.

In the days that followed, Mary lovingly cared for the Baby Jesus and thought about everything the angel had told her about who he was and what he would become. The innkeeper's wife helped her, bringing food, singing to the child, and making sure he had plenty of warm, clean clothes.

People began to come to the stable to visit the baby because the shepherds had told everyone they met of the miracle they had seen. Some didn't believe the story, but others came in and knelt at the manger in worship. Mary smiled on them all but remained silent during their visits.

Then, one day, an amazing thing happened. The innkeeper's wife ran in with the news that three grand men had arrived, asking about the newborn king. They had brought with them the most wondrous gifts, she said.

But that is a story for another night. It's time now to sleep and to dream about the beautiful baby born so many years ago in a land far away.

THE END

Wasn't that a wonderful story? Let's see how well you remember it.

Who did the angel tell to go to the stable to see the Baby Jesus?

Was it the innkeeper?

Was it the cattle?

Was it the sheep?

Was it the shepherds?

That's right, it was the shepherds. Very good. Let's try another one.

Where did Mary lay down the Baby Jesus?

Was it on the ground?

Was it on a rug?

Was it on a pillow?

Was it in a manger?

You're right, it was a manger. Now it's time to sleep just like the Baby Jesus did. Sweet dreams.

For more Quizmas trivia questions on this story,
see page 130.

The Three Kings

Are you ready for another Christmas story tonight?
This story is about three great kings who traveled a long,
long way to bring the first Christmas gifts to the Baby Jesus.
Would you like to hear about their adventures?
Before we start, see if you can answer this question.

Your Quizmas Question

Who did the Three Kings go to see?

Was it an angel?

Was it a shepherd?

Was it the Baby Jesus?

Was it their mothers?

Let's turn the page and see if you're right.

Your Quizmas Answer

You got it right! It was the Baby Jesus!
Now let's settle back and read this amazing story together.

*T*his is a story about three great kings who followed a star in the sky to find the Baby Jesus and give him the first Christmas presents.

The first king was named Balthasar. He was a tall and kind man who ruled over the kingdom of Ethiopia in Africa. His country was very beautiful, a land of mountains and valleys. There were broad plains, where lions and elephants roamed, and jungles, where monkeys swung through the trees and hippos swam in the rivers.

Balthasar lived in a splendid palace—the most beautiful you could ever imagine. He walked through halls of gleaming white marble across floors that sparkled with specks of gold. His food was served on plates of the finest silver from the great mines in the mountains. He sat on a throne decorated with every kind of precious stone you could think of: red rubies, green emeralds, blue sapphires, amber topaz, and, in the middle of the throne's back, a dazzling crystal-white diamond almost as big as his head.

As you can see, Balthasar was a very rich king! But you may be surprised to learn that he didn't really care about all this wealth and splendor. Not at all! What Balthasar loved most of all was the magnificent land over which he ruled. Nowhere else in the world could be so wonderful, he believed.

Beneath the balcony outside his bedroom, a great plain stretched away for as far as the eye could see. In the daytime, thousands of animals roamed the plain, feeding on the lush grasses—zebras and giraffes and antelopes and buffalos. He would sit and watch them for hours.

But it was the night that he loved most, because that was when the animals came to the small pond below the palace. Balthasar watched in the moonlight as the wildebeests and the warthogs drank their fill. He listened to the trumpeting of the elephants and the howling of the monkeys. He shivered at the strange laughing sound of the hyenas. And he bowed his head with respect when the great lions roared because, like him, they were kings.

Then one night, when he stepped out on his balcony, a strange thing happened. Everything seemed much brighter than usual. In fact, it was almost like daylight. He looked at the animals at the pond and they seemed just as confused as he was.

"This is very odd," he said to himself. "There is only a quarter-moon tonight. Why is everything so bright?"

He looked up at the sky and there he saw the most amazing thing—a star shining so brightly that it was almost like the sun. He shook his head in wonder. What could this be?

Balthasar called for the court astrologer to come to him. A few minutes later, a tiny man with long gray hair arrived. He was very wise and had spent his whole life studying the heavens. The king pointed at the mysterious star and watched as the man's eyes turned as big as dinner plates.

"Your Majesty, I … I … I have n-n-never seen such a thing," he stammered. "It is a great sign. I shall have to study my old scrolls to see what it means."

"Go and do so," Balthasar commanded. "Return to me at this time tomorrow with the answer."

The astrologer bowed and left, leaving the king alone to gaze at the wondrous star.

The next night, as Balthasar stood on his balcony, the astrologer returned. The great star was again shining in the same place. It was so bright that Balthasar could see all the way to the far-off mountains.

"So what have you to tell me?" asked the king.

"There is no doubt, Your Majesty. The star tells of the birth of the greatest king the world has ever seen."

"Greater even than me?" Balthasar asked.

The astrologer was very afraid, but he bowed his head and answered truthfully. "Yes, Your Majesty. Greater than any king who has ever walked the earth."

To the astrologer's surprise and relief, Balthasar did not order that he be punished for these words. Instead, the king looked at the star for a long time and then said softly, "If that is the case, then I must go and honor him. Where can I find him?"

"You have only to follow the star," said the astrologer. "Follow the star and it will lead you to him."

The next morning, Balthasar began preparing for the journey. As the word spread through the palace, everyone wanted to go with the king, but he chose only a small group to travel with him, so they could move quickly: three of his best soldiers for protection, a cook to prepare the food, a stable hand to attend to the horses they would ride on, and, of course, the little astrologer, to help find the way.

He ordered that everything be made ready as quickly as possible: water, food, feed for the horses, and any other supplies they would need.

"And I must bring a fine gift to this great king," he thought to himself. "What shall it be?"

He considered many possibilities. Perhaps a caged lion? But no, that would scare the young king, and anyway lions should run free. Maybe a giant diamond? But what would a child do with that? In the end he decided to bring a very rare gift: the finest myrrh in his kingdom. Myrrh was an ointment used to heal the sick, which was the greatest thing one person could do for another.

Two days later, the seven men set out across the plain on their way toward the distant mountains and the greatest adventure of their lives.

At that same time, in a desert land far away, there lived another king, named Melchior. The name of his country was Arabia, and it was a place where almost everything was sand. There were plains of sand and mountains of sand and even rivers of sand. When the wind blew, the sandstorms were so terrible that people had to cover their faces with a cloth to breathe.

It was a dry land with very little water, but to Melchior it was the finest place anywhere. He found beauty everywhere he looked—in the tiny desert flowers that sprouted after a rare rainstorm, in the swaying palm trees of the oases where cool springs of water bubbled, in the glowing sunsets that turned the clouds into ribbons of red and gold.

Melchior had lived for many years. He had a tanned, leathery face and a long white beard. His people loved him, for he was very wise and just.

This king did not live in a palace, at least not the kind we know. Rather, he lived in a great white tent made of the finest silk. His tent was filled with the fragrance of beautiful perfume, known as incense. His throne was made of soft, down-filled pillows, where he sat to hear the requests of his people.

On the same night that Balthasar went out on his balcony to watch the animals drinking, Melchior was traveling across the desert sands on his camel to meet some of his people who lived far away. He always rode at night, when the desert was cool, using the stars to guide him. He knew the skies well, for he had studied the stars ever since he was a little boy, learning from his father, who had learned from his father, who had learned— well, let's just say his ancestors had been watching the stars for hundreds and hundreds of years.

But tonight, something was different. A very bright star shone where he had never seen one before. What was even stranger was that it seemed to be blinking and moving very, very slowly.

Although he had never seen a star like this, Melchior knew right away what it meant. He remembered the story passed down over the years that the birth of the king of kings would be revealed by a star that would outshine all others.

Melchior was a king who made fast decisions. He raised his hand and brought his small caravan to a stop.

"Behold yonder star," he called to his followers. "It is a wonder that has been foretold, and we shall follow it and pay our respects to the greatest of all kings."

And so Melchior and the others turned their camels in the direction of the great star and began their long, long trek across the sands.

With him, he carried his greatest treasure, a golden box that his grandfather had given him. It was the dearest thing to him, and he knew it would make a fine gift for a new king.

The third king was named Gaspar. He was a handsome man who at a very young age had come to the throne of Tarsus, a city on a wide river that led to the sea. Every day, great ships sailed up and down beneath the windows of his palace, carrying fruits and vegetables from the surrounding farms to feed people in other parts of the world.

Gaspar was a man of the sea. From the time he was a little boy, his father, the old king, had taught him how to sail, and Gaspar loved nothing more than being out on a boat with the wind in his face. His palace reflected his love of the water. It faced toward the river and the sea beyond, so the smell of salt air could come in on the breeze. At the entrance, a great fountain greeted visitors. Inside were many small courtyards with quiet pools. Models of ships of every kind lined the halls, and the floors were decorated with beautiful seashells. His throne was carved from wood that had once been part of his father's favorite boat.

Once a year, Gaspar would leave his beautiful palace and travel on one of his ships to a distant land. He loved to look up and see the great sails billowing in the breeze and to feel the deck rolling beneath his feet as the graceful ship sliced through the waves. On these trips, he worked as hard as any member of the crew because, as he said, "If I am to help my people, I must first know them."

When he was at sea he often would go on deck at night to look at the stars and to make sure the ship was traveling in the right direction. On one such night, he saw something amazing. Low on the horizon, a great star had appeared, so bright that it outshone everything in the sky. He blinked, not believing what he saw. But when he opened his eyes the star was still there, brighter than ever.

He called for the ship's captain to come and see this wonder, and together they stared in awe. Then the captain, an elderly man who had served Gaspar's father, fell to his knees and said, "It is the sign."

"What sign, ancient one?" demanded the king. Thereupon, the captain told Gaspar of a folk tale passed down over many, many years about how the lord of the world would come, and the sign of his birth would be a star that would be bigger and brighter than anything in the sky, even the moon.

Gaspar immediately decided to go and pay his respects to this wondrous king.

"Turn the ship toward the star," he ordered the captain, "for we shall follow it wherever it may lead."

Then he thought to himself, "I will need a gift to present to this great king. What should it be?"

The answer came immediately. On the ship was a box of frankincense, a rare perfume used only in the most special ceremonies. It would be Gaspar's offering to the newborn king.

The Three Kings traveled for many, many days following the star, which was so bright they could see it even in daytime. After sailing on and on over the waves, Gaspar's ship finally docked at a small port, where he bought camels to continue to follow the star on land. Four days later, he and his men rested outside the walls of the great city of Jerusalem, a holy place that he had never before visited.

On one side of him was the tent of an old man with a flowing white beard, who Gaspar soon learned was also a king, named Melchior. On the other side was the camp of a tall, dark-skinned man named Balthasar, who, it turned out, was a king as well.

The Three Kings were surprised to learn that each of them had followed the star to come to this place, so far from their homes.

"We must join together to complete our journey and pay our respects to the new king," Gaspar said.

They all agreed. But Melchior, being the oldest, said, "First, we must visit King Herod, who rules within Jerusalem, for it is only proper that we inform him of our journey."

The next day, the Three Kings passed through the walls and entered Jerusalem. They immediately went to Herod's palace.

Now, King Herod was not a good man. He was vain and greedy and often told lies. So he was very suspicious when the Three Kings came before him.

"Why have you traveled so far to come here?" he asked.

Melchior, as the oldest of the three, answered, "We have all seen a great star in the sky that tells of the birth of the king of kings. We have come to honor and to praise him."

"Do you know where we may find him?" Balthasar asked.

Herod was deeply troubled when he heard this but tried to hide his feelings from his visitors.

"I have not heard of this new king," he answered. "But go and search for him and if you find him, return here and tell me where he is so that I may go and give praise to him as well."

With that, he dismissed the three with a wave of his hand.

The Three Kings returned to their camp.

"What shall we do now?" asked Gaspar.

"We shall continue to do as we have done," answered Melchior. "The great star has brought us this far. I have faith that it will lead us the rest of the way."

That night, they set out together on camels, just the three of them, following the star to its final destination.

And, sure enough, it led them right to the stable in Bethlehem where the Baby Jesus lay in his manger.

When the Three Kings saw the star stop in the sky and shine its light down onto the stable, they knew their long journey had ended.

They reverently entered the stable, bearing the gifts they had brought from afar. Together they kneeled before the manger and worshipped the babe while Mary and Joseph and all the stable animals watched in silence.

They stayed a long time, for they knew they were in the presence of a wonder they would never know again. Then, just as dawn was about to break, they rose, bowed one more time, and took their leave.

No one said a word as they mounted their camels and left the village. But one more miracle awaited them.

As they turned their camels back toward Jerusalem, they heard the sound of trumpets. Then there was a burst of light and suddenly an angel stood before them, blocking their way.

"Do not return to Herod," the angel warned, "for he has lied to you. He wishes to harm the Baby Jesus. Return to your lands another way."

And then the angel was gone and all was quiet again.

The Three Kings turned to one another.

"We must do as the angel has commanded," Melchior said.

"Nothing must harm the newborn king," Balthasar agreed.

"Let us send a message to our followers to meet us elsewhere," Gaspar added. "That way the child shall be safe."

And so the Three Kings turned their camels away from Jerusalem and rode toward the dawn, carrying in their hearts the memory of a magical night that would remain with them for the rest of their days.

THE END

Did you like the story of the Three Kings? Would you like to try to answer a question about the story? Here's one.

What were the Three Kings riding when they entered Bethlehem?

Were they on zebras?

Were they on hippos?

Were they on elephants?

Were they on camels?

Of course, they were riding on camels. Would you like to try another?

What led the Three Kings to the Baby Jesus?

Was it a boat?

Was it the sun?

Was it a star?

Was it the moon?

That's right, it was a star. And that's all for tonight. Sleep well.

For more Quizmas trivia questions on this story, see page 134.

The Christmas Animals

It's time for tonight's Christmas story, so let's get comfy. All right, are you ready? For the last two nights we've been reading about the birth of the Baby Jesus and the Three Kings who brought him gifts. Tonight, we'll read about all the animals in the stable that night when the Christ Child was born. Would you like that? Now, before we start, let's see if you can answer this question. Think back to the first story we read and you'll remember the answer.

Your Quizmas Question

What kind of animal did Mary ride on her journey to Bethlehem?

Was it a camel?

Was it a horse?

Was it an elephant?

Was it a donkey?

Let's look on the next page and see.

Your Quizmas Answer

That's right, it was a donkey. So why don't we begin
by reading more about the donkey and what happened
to him after he arrived at the stable.

*T*he little brown donkey was very, very tired. His big pointy ears were flopping and his long tail drooped almost to the ground. His sad brown eyes could hardly see anything through the darkness and the rain, and he could barely lift his feet.

It had been a long day. Joseph and Mary had begun the journey to Bethlehem as soon as the sun was up. Except for some short rests along the way, they had been traveling the whole time, Joseph walking ahead and Mary riding the little donkey.

"We should try to get there by tonight," Joseph had told Mary as they set off. "I know it's a long way, but the baby could come at any time. I want to make sure you're warm and comfortable when that happens."

And so they started out. At first it was easy for the little brown donkey as they traveled through fields and orchards where the ground was flat. The little donkey could have gone even faster, but he decided to move slowly to make the ride smoother and more comfortable for Mary.

But when they came to the hills, it got harder. The road turned into a narrow trail, covered with rocks of all sizes. The little brown donkey had to pick his way carefully to avoid a stumble that might cause Mary to fall and hurt herself. All afternoon, his big dark eyes watched the road carefully. Watch out for that big stone! Be careful of the loose pebbles! Don't slip!

At one point, a snake slithered in front of him, hissing as it went. Normally, the little brown donkey would have been very frightened and might have run away. But when he remembered Mary riding on his back, he felt surprisingly calm. Instead of running, he simply stopped and waited while Joseph shooed the snake away. He thought he heard Mary whisper, "My brave little donkey," but he couldn't be sure. And so they went on.

Then it started to rain, and that's when it became really, really hard. With water running into his eyes, the little brown donkey could hardly see the way. The light began to fade and the sky became darker. Suddenly it was night—a wet, black, moonless night. The little donkey wanted to stop, but he knew he couldn't. They *had* to get to Bethlehem!

And then Mary spoke to him, very quietly, in a soft, beautiful voice.

"It's not far now, my little friend," she said. "You have been so good and so careful all day. I know you can do it."

With that, the little brown donkey suddenly felt strong again. Of course he could do it! *Of course he could!* Even though he could not see clearly, he moved steadily forward, and, miraculously, every step was the right one. He missed every rock, every spot of soft gravel, even every little pebble. It was as if someone was directing each of his feet to just the right spot in the trail—and perhaps someone was!

All of a sudden, there it was. In the valley below them they could see the town of Bethlehem outlined against the night sky. Most of the town was dark, but toward the center of the village was a patch of welcoming light. Joseph guided the little donkey down the last hillside, and within a few minutes they were standing in front of the inn.

Now, when the donkey heard the innkeeper say there was no room for Mary and Joseph, he felt so sad that he almost cried—if donkeys could cry, that is.

But when the kind man directed them to the stable at the back of the inn, the little donkey's heart leapt. He knew it would be a warm place and he would find other friendly animals there.

Sure enough, when they arrived and Mary got off, the other animals greeted the little donkey. Since most of them had never been outside the stable, they had lots of questions for him.

"*Cluck, cluck* … where have you come from?" cackled the hen.

"*Bzzzzzz* … and how wazzzzzz your trip?" buzzed the bees.

"*Cock-a-doodle-doo* … and what was in the big world outside?" crowed the rooster.

The little brown donkey wanted to answer all their questions, but he was just *toooo* tired. "*Hee-haw* … I'll tell you all about it tomorrow," he brayed. And with that he lay down on the straw and fell fast asleep.

Now, normally the little brown donkey wouldn't have stirred again until dawn—he was *that* tired. But at midnight, something very strange happened. The whole stable was suddenly filled with bright light, almost as if the sun had come right in the door. It woke the little donkey, and he immediately knew that something very wonderful had happened.

Bounding up, he quickly went to the front of the stable. All the other animals were gathered there, which surprised him, as they should have been asleep at this time. He pushed his way through them, and then he saw a wondrous sight. Mary was sitting by a manger. Lying in the straw was her newborn baby, a beautiful little boy with a face so calm and peaceful and glowing that even the little donkey knew the baby was very, very special.

The bright light that filled the room seemed to come from the babe himself. The little donkey didn't understand how this could be, but something inside told him this was a child like no other the world had ever seen. It was, of course, the Baby Jesus.

So the little donkey did something no animal had ever done before. He folded his front legs under him, lowered his shaggy head, and bowed down to show his love and respect. When all the other animals saw what the little donkey had done, they too bowed down before the Baby Jesus.

For a long time the stable was silent, although the donkey thought he saw Mary's lips form the words "Thank you, little friend." And then the stillness was broken by the arrival at the stable of a group of shepherds, who said an angel had told them to come.

Now, while the shepherds gathered around the Baby Jesus, the strangest thing happened. We all know that animals and birds can't talk, don't we? Well, on this magical night they suddenly found they could speak in human voices. The birds nesting in the rafters flew down, and the animals huddled close together and started talking about what they could do for the little baby in the manger.

"I will stand close so that my breath will keep him warm," said the ox.

"I too will help keep him warm by fanning the fire with my wings," said the robin.

"And I will offer wool from my coat," said the sheep.

"I will sing the baby to sleep with a beautiful lullaby," said the nightingale.

"I will go to the rooftop at first light and tell the world that Christ is born," said the rooster.

"We will all hum his praises together," said the bees.

"I will give him milk," said the cow.

"I will lay eggs for him," said the hen.

"When he is older, I will carry him anywhere he wants to go," said the horse. The little brown donkey scowled at that!

But the big white stork was silent. Nervously, she shifted from one foot to the other, wondering what gift she could possibly give to the Baby Jesus.

You see, the stork is one of the largest birds in the world, but when it isn't flying it looks awkward and rather ugly. This particular stork was very mindful of that. She had made her nest on the roof of the stable, where she was sitting on four big white eggs. Normally, she never would have left the nest, but when she heard all the excitement below her and saw the bright light coming from the stable entrance, curiosity got the better of her and she flew down to see what was happening.

Now she stood at the edge of the animal gathering, first on one foot, then on the other foot, then on the first foot again. What could she say? What could she offer?

She looked across the stable at Joseph and Mary and all the shepherds around the Baby Jesus and she felt *sooo* sad. She wanted so much to do something useful, but what?

She couldn't sing like the nightingale.

She couldn't give milk like the cow.

She couldn't carry the Baby Jesus like the horse.

What could she do?

She thought and she thought and she thought.

And then she had an idea!

The ox was going to breathe on the Baby Jesus to keep him warm. The robin was going to use his little wings to fan the fire. The sheep was going to offer her wool.

She too could help to warm the baby—and make his bed much softer and more comfortable. The straw on which he lay was hard and prickly. She could fix that!

Bending down, she used her beak to pluck one of her big, soft feathers from her breast. Then she plucked another, and another, and another. Soon her beak was filled with fluffy white down.

She slowly made her way across the stable, stood in front of Mary, and dropped the feathers at her feet.

Mary knew right away what the stork had done and why. She smiled at the bird, picked up the feathers, and began to line the manger with them. Soon the Baby Jesus was lying on a bed of warm, cozy feathers, as soft and smooth as the finest silk.

The stork felt her heart swell. She was happier than she had ever been in her life. She had done something very wonderful— just like the ox, just like the sheep, just like the donkey, just like the robin, just like all the other birds and animals.

It had been a strange night, she thought, as she flew back to her nest to wait for the birth of her own little babies. A strange night and a very wonderful one!

And what about the little brown donkey? What happened to him?

Because he had been so careful on the journey and had showed such love and respect for the Baby Jesus, he had earned a special place in Mary's heart.

So when it came time to leave the stable with the Baby Jesus, Mary politely said no when the innkeeper offered to let her ride the big horse.

"I will ride on my little donkey," she said. "He has proven himself to be brave and faithful, and I trust him to carry us safely over even the hardest trails."

In all the world, no animal has ever been as pleased and proud as the little brown donkey was at that moment. After that, he carried Mary and the Baby Jesus for many, many miles. He never once missed a step. He never once stumbled. He never once ran from a snake. And he never again got tired!

Of course, all of this happened many, many years ago. But do you know that to this very day some people say that if you are out in the fields at midnight on Christmas Eve you can hear the animals talking?

Others say that on Christmas Eve all the bees in the world hum together to praise the Baby Jesus.

Some people believe the reason the robin has a red breast is that he got burned when he was fanning the fire in the stable with his wings.

And ever since anyone can remember, the stork has been said to be the bird that safely delivers all new babies to their mommies and daddies.

The mother stork that gave her soft feathers to line the manger of the Baby Jesus would have been very proud.

THE END

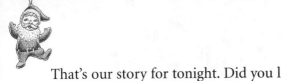

That's our story for tonight. Did you like it? Would you like to try to answer some questions about it? Here's one.

Which animal offered to breathe on the Baby Jesus to keep him warm?

Was it the sheep?

Was it the horse?

Was it the ox?

Was it the hen?

That's right, it was the ox. Let's try another one.

Which bird offered to sing the Baby Jesus to sleep?

Was it the rooster?

Was it the hen?

Was it the stork?

Was it the nightingale?

It was the nightingale, which has one of the sweetest songs you'll ever hear.

All right, it's time to go to sleep now. Tomorrow night, if you're very, very good, we'll read a story about a grumpy old man who didn't like Christmas at all. Can you imagine anyone like that? Good night now. Sleep well.

For more Quizmas trivia questions on this story,
see page 138.

A
Christmas
Carol

Tonight we're going to read another kind of Christmas story.
This one takes place many, many years after the birth of
the Baby Jesus. It's about a man named Ebenezer Scrooge
and some very strange things that happened
to him one Christmas Eve.
Before we start, here's a question for you.

Your Quizmas Question

Who was Ebenezer Scrooge?

Was he a handsome prince?

Was he a naughty little boy?

Was he Santa's best friend?

Was he a mean old man who hated Christmas?

Let's turn the page for the answer.

Your Quizmas Answer

That's right. Ebenezer Scrooge was a mean
old man who hated Christmas.
He's also the main character in a book written more than a
hundred years ago by a famous writer named Charles Dickens.
The book is called *A Christmas Carol,* and even though it's about
Christmas, there's also a little bit of Halloween mixed up in the
tale. Are you ready for a Christmas ghost story?
Don't be scared—it has a happy ending! Let's read it together.

"*B*ah humbug!" grumbled the mean old man, watching a troop of merry carolers stroll by his office window. He looked away and stuck two bony fingers in his ears to block out their singing. The happy sound of Christmas music always gave him a pounding headache. Only once the carolers were out of sight did he go back to counting his money.

Snow fell lightly in the darkening streets. It was late into the afternoon of December 24—Christmas Eve—and Ebenezer Scrooge could feel the holiday creeping closer and closer like a grimy little bug making its way toward him across the floor. He hated everything about Christmas. He hated the candy canes on the trees, he hated the stockings by the fireplace, he hated the festive turkey dinner, and, most of all, he hated the presents.

"Spend ... buy ... spend ... give! Some holiday!" he snorted, closing up his cash box with a satisfying snap of the metal lid. "If you ask me, it's all about stealing my hard-earned money!"

A gentle knocking interrupted his penny-pinching thoughts. Frowning, Scrooge looked up from his desk to see his clerk, Bob Cratchit, poking his head through the doorway of the office.

"Um ... mind if I leave a little early tonight, sir?" he asked meekly.

Scrooge glared at his pocket watch.

"You want to leave *now*?" he barked. "There are still twenty minutes left of the workday!"

"But ... but sir, it's Christmas Eve!"

Shuddering at the mere mention of the holiday, Scrooge threw up his hands in disgust.

"Ugh! Fine, go home!"

"Thank you, sir ... and merry Christmas," squeaked Bob. "Looks like it's going to be a white one."

"Just more slush to shovel off my walkway!" Only Ebenezer Scrooge could find something bad about Christmas Eve snow!

Once all his work was done, Scrooge shrugged on his coat, locked up his office, and trudged off into the night. He ate a lonely dinner in his usual lonely restaurant, then went home to his lonely bed.

"Merry Christmas!" smiled a passing stranger on the street.

"Bah humbug!" mumbled Ebenezer, shooting the man a nasty look as he quickened his pace toward home. Scrooge lived by himself in a big empty house, a house that was cold and dark during the long winter months, but especially cold and especially dark on Christmas Eve. Unlike every other house in town, there was no celebration here tonight—no tree covered in decorations, no candles burning in the window, and no delicious dinner waiting on the table.

As he arrived home, something very strange happened. Just as Scrooge was putting his key into the lock, the door knocker changed into a face right before his eyes! And not just any face, but a creepy, scary, ghostly face that reminded him of his old business partner, Jacob Marley.

"What's this?" wondered Scrooge, taking a nervous step back. The face was not angry or ferocious, but looked like a bad lobster in a dark cellar. And then, as he was taking a closer look, it changed back into a knocker again.

"Pooh, pooh!" mumbled Scrooge as he closed the door with a bang. He plodded slowly up the stairs, his footsteps echoing loudly through the empty house.

Creeeeeeeak went the door as Scrooge entered his gloomy bedroom. It was icy cold because he wouldn't spend money to keep the fire going. Shivering, he changed quickly into his nightshirt and went to bed.

Just as he was drifting off to sleep, the eerie sound of rattling chains filled the air.

Ka-chunk—ka-chink—ka-chunk

Startled, Scrooge sat up in bed. The sound came closer and grew louder until it seemed like it was right on top of him.

KA-CHUNK—KA-CHINK—KA-CHUNK

"Who's there?" Scrooge yelped, peering through the darkness.

"*Whoooooooo!*" came a hollow, haunted voice in his ear.

Scrooge jumped with fright and almost fell onto the floor. "Leave me alone or I'll send for the police!" he shouted, pulling the blanket over his head.

But the voice refused to go away.

"Ebenezer Scrooge!" it howled. "Don't you recognize me?"

Trembling with fear, Scrooge lowered the blanket and came face to face with the gray, glowing ghost of Jacob Marley. Floating above Scrooge's bed, Marley was dressed in a thin white robe and covered in a long rope of heavy chains.

"J-J-J-Jacob … is that you?" Scrooge whispered. He had never seen a ghost before and he was very afraid.

"Yes, Ebenezer, it's me," the ghost replied, his pale face shining brightly in the dark, dingy room.

"W-w-what are you doing here? And why are you covered in chains?"

The ghost of Jacob Marley suddenly looked sad and ashamed.

"These chains are my punishment for being such a mean, stingy man when I was alive. There's one link for every greedy thing I ever did in my life. I have to walk the earth carrying them forever and ever and ever. Can you imagine how heavy they are, Ebenezer?" he wailed, holding them up and rattling them in Scrooge's face.

KA-CHUNK—KA-CHINK—KA-CHUNK

"I'm sorry for you, Jacob," said Scrooge, backing away from the chains, "b-b-but what does that have to do with me?"

"It has everything to do with you, Ebenezer," the ghost howled, "because the same thing is going to happen to you if you don't change *your* greedy ways!"

Scrooge picked up his blanket and tried to hide again, but the ghost of Jacob Marley pulled it away.

"Three ghosts will be coming to visit you soon," he warned, pointing a glowing gray finger in Scrooge's face. "Pay close attention to what they have to show you."

"But w-w-why, Jacob, why?"

"Because they might be able to save you from your own chains of greed. There's no hope left for me, but there just might be some left for you."

And with those words hanging in the air, the ghost of Jacob Marley disappeared like a puff of smoke into the wind. Still shaking with fear, Scrooge lay back down in his bed and pulled the blankets up over his ears. It was a long time before he was able to fall asleep.

Ding ... dong ... ding!

The sound of a church bell outside his window woke Scrooge from his sleep. He sat up in bed and looked around his dark room.

Had the ghost of Jacob Marley really come to visit him, or had it all been a dream? A second later, he had the answer. With a flash of light, a small old man appeared in the room. He had big ears and a round little tummy and wore a pointy cap over his white hair. From his long robe and gray, glowing skin, Scrooge knew right away that this was the first of the three ghosts Marley had warned of.

"*Scroooooge!* I am the Ghost of Christmas Past," announced the old man. "I have so much to show you and very little time. Come away with me now...."

And then, placing Scrooge's hand over his heart, the ghost carried him away to a time long before—a time when Ebenezer was a much younger man, a time when he was happier and much less greedy. He showed him a brightly lit room filled with happy people who were singing and dancing as they celebrated Christmas. And there, right in the middle, dancing with a pretty girl, was Scrooge as a young man, laughing and talking and having a grand old time.

"See? You weren't always so mean and lonely, Scrooge," the ghost reminded him. "Your life took a turn for the worse when you started caring more about money than about people."

And with that, the ghost took him back to his bedroom and disappeared.

Ding … dong … ding!

The church bell woke Scrooge again. Had another day come and gone? Was the second ghost here?

He opened his sleepy eyes and saw a light shining from outside his bedroom door. Stumbling across the floor in his bare feet, he walked into a beautiful room that had been decorated for a Christmas party. Waiting there for him was a glowing giant wearing a green robe trimmed with white fur and with a holly wreath on his head.

"*Scroooooge!* I am the Ghost of Christmas Present," announced the giant in a loud, booming voice. "There's something important you must see, so come away with me now…." And placing Scrooge's hand on the edge of his robe, he carried him away to a little house on the other side of town. Looking through the window, Scrooge realized right away that it was the home of his office clerk.

"This is Bob Cratchit's house. What are we doing here?" he asked.

But the ghost held a giant finger up to his giant lips and motioned for Scrooge to keep quiet and listen.

The Cratchit family was sitting around their table, enjoying a Christmas meal of goose and pudding. Even though their plates were half-empty and the room was bare and plain, the house was bubbling over with happiness. Bob and his wife had six children, varying in size from very big to very small. But the smallest child, a little boy named Tim, looked thin and frail and had a crutch propped up beside his chair. Tiny Tim sat close to his father, who held his little hand tightly, as if he worried that his son might be taken away from him. In his other hand Bob held up his glass and said, "A merry Christmas to us all, my dears. God bless us!"

"Yes, God bless us, every one!" echoed Tiny Tim, with a weak little cough.

"What's the matter with that boy?" whispered Scrooge with a worried frown.

"That's Tiny Tim. He's very sick and there's no money for medicine," explained the ghost. "Unless things change, he won't live much longer."

Scrooge took a closer look at poor Tiny Tim, who was smiling and cheerful even through his pain. He suddenly felt overcome with sadness for the little boy and wished he could do something to help. But before he had the chance to say anything, the giant ghost disappeared and the third and final ghost was coming toward him.

This one was the scariest ghost of all. He wore a long black robe with a hood that covered his face, and although he spoke not a word, he brought with him a sense of doom and gloom. Scrooge was very afraid.

"Y-y-you must be the Ghost of Christmas Yet to Come," he said, his voice trembling with fright.

But the ghost still didn't say a word. He just pointed a shriveled, dark finger straight in front of him and led Scrooge to a creepy graveyard. Together they walked past row after row of tombstones until they came to one lonely grave, set off on its own. Overrun with weeds, the grave appeared to have been completely forgotten by the rest of the world.

Scrooge's legs were shaking with terror as he looked around.

"Why are we here?" he asked. "Whose grave is this?"

But still the ghost said nothing. Instead, he led Scrooge closer and closer until the name on the tombstone became clear.

It read simply: EBENEZER SCROOGE.

Scrooge sank to his knees and started to cry.

"Am I going to die all alone? Won't anybody care about me? Oh please, Mr. Ghost, is this the way it has to be? Is there still time to change this future you've shown me?"

But the ghost still said nothing.

"Please!" howled Scrooge, clutching at the ghost's long robe. "I have learned my lesson, I promise. I will honor Christmas in my heart and try to keep it there all year long! I will be good and kind and generous. Just please give me another chance!"

With those words, the ghost's robe magically turned into a bedsheet. And yes, the bedsheet was Scrooge's, and so was the bed and so was the room. The night was over, the ghosts were gone, it was Christmas morning, and he was back home!

"Thank you for my second chance, ghosts! Thank you, Jacob Marley!" cried Scrooge, springing out of bed. "I am as light as a feather, I am as happy as an angel. A merry Christmas to everybody! A happy New Year to all the world!"

And right then and there something amazing happened. Ebenezer Scrooge decided to start being a good person instead of a mean one. Excited for this second chance to live a better life, he ran to the window and stuck out his head.

"Excuse me, young man!" he called out to a boy walking on the street below. "Do you know where the grocery store is one street over?"

"Yes, I do," answered the boy.

"Wonderful!" said Scrooge. "And do you know whether they've sold the prize turkey that was hanging up there? Not the little turkey—the big one?"

"What, the one as big as me?" replied the boy. "Yes, it's still there."

"Good! I want you to go and buy it for me! Here's some money!" he said, tossing a handful of coins out the window. The boy scrambled to pick them up and ran off down the street like a shot. When he came back with the turkey, Scrooge had it sent right over to Bob Cratchit's house as a Christmas present. Then, the very next day, he gave Bob a big raise in pay. And for Tiny Tim, he paid for medicine and the best doctors in the country until the little boy was all better.

Ebenezer Scrooge became as good a friend, as good a boss, and as good a man as anyone ever knew in the whole wide world.

And the ghosts never came to visit him ever again.

And so, as Tiny Tim observed, God bless us, every one!

THE END

Did you like that story? Would you like to see how well you remember it? Let's see if you can answer this question.

What was the name of Scrooge's old business partner, the ghost who carried a long rope of heavy chains?

Was it Jason Barley?

Was it Johnnie Farley?

Was it Humbug Charley?

Was it Jacob Marley?

Jacob Marley. That's very good. Do you want to try another one?

What was the name of the sick little boy who needed medicine?

Was it Little Jim?

Was it Teeny Tom?

Was it Tiny Tim?

Was it Small Sam?

Very good, it was Tiny Tim. Now it's time to say good night to Ebenezer Scrooge and Tiny Tim and go to sleep because our own Christmas will be here very soon.

*For more Quizmas trivia questions on this story,
see page 142.*

The Nutcracker

Tonight, we're going to read another story about Christmas.
But before we start, see if you know the answer to this question.
If you don't, we'll find the answer in the story.

Your Quizmas Question

What does a nutcracker do?

Does it open bottles?

Does it open cans?

Does it open presents?

Does it open nuts?

Let's turn the page and find out.

Your Quizmas Answer

Of course, it cracks open nuts. Tonight we're going
to read a story about a very special nutcracker, one who
fought a battle with a Mouse King … and won!
It's a funny little Christmas tale about children, dolls,
candy, and, of course, mice. Let's read it together now.

*M*arie and her older brother, Fritz, were huddled by the window in their playroom. They peeked out from behind the curtains and watched the snow falling lightly onto the evergreen trees outside. It was Christmas Eve and it was just beginning to get dark. Marie and Fritz hugged each other with glee. They could barely contain their excitement!

Earlier that day, they had both seen their godfather Drosselmeier come into the house carrying a giant box, so big it was almost twice his size. Their godfather was a short little man with a face wrinkled like a raisin and a puffy white wig on his head. Over one eye he wore a black patch, just like a pirate. But he wasn't a pirate at all. As far as the children were concerned, he was the best toy maker in the entire world. Every year at Christmas, Godfather Drosselmeier made them a beautiful new toy.

"What do you think he's making us this year?" whispered Marie, bursting with excitement. Their godfather had arrived earlier that morning, and the wonderful sound of hammering and banging had been echoing through the walls all day long. She didn't know if she could wait much longer to see what he'd made.

"Maybe it's a fort with lots of marching soldiers!" guessed Fritz, who loved playing with toy soldiers.

"Or maybe it's a garden with a lake and beautiful swans!" Marie said hopefully in a dreamy voice.

Just then, a bell rang, the doors opened up, and their mother and father appeared in the room.

"Merry Christmas, children!" they cried, wrapping up Marie and Fritz in a big hug. "Come and see what presents are waiting for you!"

The children didn't have to be asked twice. Tingling with expectation, they followed their parents to the parlor, for in their home they always opened their presents on Christmas Eve.

In the middle of the room was a big, beautiful Christmas tree, covered from top to bottom in lights and goodies and decorations. Under the tree were stacks of the most incredible presents. There were dolls for Marie and a horsy for Fritz and oodles and oodles of candies and piles and piles of picture books. The two of them must have been very good children all year to deserve presents like these.

They played with them for a while, and then a bell rang again and Godfather Drosselmeier came in with the most special present of all.

"Merry Christmas, Godfather! What have you brought for us?" they cried. Their godfather walked across the room and placed the big box in front of them. When they opened it up, they found inside a beautiful wooden castle with windows and towers and dozens of little wooden people dressed up in perfect little clothes. Fritz and Marie clapped their hands with happiness, for they had never seen anything like it before. But by far the most unusual thing in the box was the strange little wooden man wearing a violet coat with white braid. His face was frozen into a big wide grin, and his big white teeth made him look like he was ready to bite into something.

"Who is this?" asked Marie, picking up the wooden man. Maybe it was his funny little face, or maybe it was his poor skinny body, but something about him made her heart fill with love and tenderness.

"He's a nutcracker," explained her godfather with a laugh. "He will crack hard nuts for you with his teeth."

Excited to try him out, Marie took a small walnut from her pile of goodies and put it carefully in the Nutcracker's mouth.

Crack!

In an instant, the hard shell was opened and the sweet nut inside was free. Marie was delighted.

"Hey, let me have a turn!" yelled Fritz, grabbing the Nutcracker from his sister. Like many little boys his age, Fritz was sometimes naughty, even on Christmas Eve. He took the biggest, hardest walnut he could find and stuffed it in the Nutcracker's mouth.

CRAAAAAACK went the nut, along with three of the Nutcracker's big white teeth.

"Oh no! You broke him!" cried Marie, taking her beloved Nutcracker back. Ever so gently she wrapped him up in a handkerchief and rocked him back and forth in her arms as if he were a hurt little baby. She held him that way for the rest of the night, not giving a second look to any of her other presents. She held him that way until it became very late and the party had come to an end and Godfather Drosselmeier had gone home.

"Now it's time for bed," announced her mother, pointing to the clock on the wall. Indeed, it was very late.

"You and Fritz go ahead," said Marie, not ready to leave the Nutcracker just yet. "I'll be up in a few more minutes."

Now, because Marie was such a good young lady, her mother felt that this would be all right.

"Just don't stay down here too long," she reminded her.

"Yes, Mother," Marie replied quietly.

Once she was all alone, she laid the Nutcracker down on the floor, unwrapped the handkerchief, and looked over his wounds.

"Don't worry, I won't let anyone hurt you ever again," she whispered tenderly, kissing his hard wooden cheek. For a second, she thought she saw the Nutcracker flash a sad smile. But she knew that was impossible, since he was only a toy. With a sigh, she picked him up again and carried him over to the toy cabinet, where she tucked him into bed with her other dolls, on the shelf right below Fritz's army of toy soldiers.

"Good night," she whispered to him with a pat on his hard wooden head. Marie had many dolls and was very good at taking care of them.

She had started up the stairs to bed when suddenly she heard strange sounds—whispering and shuffling and giggling and squeaking.

Now, what do you think was making those noises?

Then dozens and dozens of tiny eyes peeked out at her through the darkness.

Who do you think those little eyes belonged to?

Did you guess mice? Then you are right! All of a sudden, hundreds of mice had filled the room and were scampering about on the floor. Marie watched them with fascination. At first she thought they were funny, but then a mouse appeared that was so strange and awful it took her breath away. This mouse had seven heads, and on each of its seven heads was a golden crown. When this Mouse King came up through a small hole in the floor, every other mouse in the room cheered. Then, arranging themselves into battle lines, they marched straight toward Marie—and her Nutcracker.

"*EEEEEEEK!*" Marie cried, as she ran to protect him. But the Nutcracker had already thrown off his blanket and jumped out of his doll's bed ready for a fight. Fritz's toy soldiers jumped down from their shelf to join him in battle. Marie gasped in surprise. Her Nutcracker was alive, along with all the other dolls in the toy cabinet!

And then the army of mice, led by the seven-headed king, and the army of toys, led by the Nutcracker, started to fight. Marie was so astounded that she couldn't move at all. And with all the confusion of smoke and dust, she could hardly see anything. But she could hear the shrill squeaking of the mice mixed with the pretty voices of her porcelain dolls as they cheered on the Nutcracker and his army.

The toys fought bravely, but in the end, the mouse army was just too big and strong to be beaten. Before long, the mice had seized the Nutcracker by his wooden arms and dragged him over to the Mouse King. Seeing this, Marie threw her slipper at the mice and screamed at the top of her lungs.

"AAAAAAAAAHHHH!"

And then she fainted away from fright.

When she woke up it was morning and she was lying in her own bed. She looked around for the Nutcracker, trying to remember what had happened to him.

"Where have all those nasty mice gone?" she asked her mother, who was standing nearby. "And where is my Nutcracker?"

"Hush now, dear," said her mother. "Your Nutcracker is safe and sound in the toy cabinet. I found you sleeping there on the floor last night."

"But he was alive and there was a big fight and the Mouse King wanted to capture him …," she protested.

"Now, now, Marie. I'm sure you just had a bad dream," said her mother, smoothing the hair away from her face. "Or perhaps you have a bit of a fever. Either way, I think you should stay in bed until you feel better."

And so, much to Marie's dismay, her mother made her stay in bed for the rest of the day. She was so bored she wanted to cry.

Sometime in the afternoon her bedroom door opened and in came Godfather Drosselmeier.

"I heard you're not feeling well," he said with a wink of his one good eye. "But I think I have something that might make you feel better."

And then from behind his back he pulled out the Nutcracker, whose broken teeth he had fixed and put back in.

"Oh, thank you!" exclaimed Marie, hugging her doll with relief. The Nutcracker smiled back at her with his big wide grin.

"But Godfather Drosselmeier," she added after a moment's

thought, "why did you make the Nutcracker with such an ugly face?"

"Well," he replied, sitting down at the foot of her bed, "that's a very long story. Are you ready to hear about Princess Pirlipat and the Hard Nut?"

Marie nodded. Since she wasn't allowed to get out of her bed, it was a perfect time to listen to a story. And here's how it went:

"Once upon a time, the King and Queen had a little baby girl," began Godfather Drosselmeier. "Her name was Princess Pirlipat, and she was the most beautiful child anyone had ever seen. But she had to be guarded closely by a team of nurses and cats to keep her safe. Why, you ask? Because there was a mouse in the palace who had threatened to bite the beautiful baby in two! This terrible rodent's name was Madam Mouserinks.

"For many months, the family kept the baby safe. But one awful night when everyone was sleeping, a nurse woke up and found Madam Mouserinks right in the baby's crib. The nurse and her cat quickly chased the mouse away, but alas it was too late. The most horrible thing had happened! Madam Mouserinks had changed the beautiful little princess into an ugly, horrible-looking creature.

"The King and Queen were very upset when they saw what had happened to their child. They called in the best doctors and scientists in the land to find a way to cure her. Finally, they discovered that to become beautiful again, the little Princess Pirlipat had to eat the sweet kernel of the Krakatuk nut.

"Now, that might sound pretty simple, but the Krakatuk was the hardest nut in the entire world! It was harder than a candy cane, harder than a seashell, harder even than the biggest, strongest rock in your backyard. Any young man who could crack it would break the ugly spell that had been put on the princess and, in return, would be promised her hand in marriage.

"And so the search was on to find the Krakatuk nut. For years and years, the searchers scoured every corner of the world with no success. Finally, after fifteen long winters, springs, summers, and falls, the Krakatuk nut was found!"

"Where?" interrupted Marie, on the edge of her bed with suspense.

"Well, if you can believe it," her godfather continued, "it was found in the city of Nuremberg, at the house of my very own nephew! Without wasting any time, my nephew went to the palace of Princess Pirlipat, who by now was a young lady and still as ugly as the day Madam Mouserinks had cast a spell over her. Confident he could break the spell, my young nephew stepped forward with the Krakatuk nut in his hand, fearlessly placed it in his mouth, and …

"CRAAAAAAAAAAAACK!

"In one single bite he broke the hard shell! Filled with pride, my nephew opened the shell, handed the kernel to the princess, and took a step back to watch. With a long, trembling breath, Pirlipat put the nut in her mouth and swallowed it. Then, wonder of wonders, she was changed back into the most beautiful princess anyone had ever seen!

"Unfortunately, however, the moment the princess became beautiful again, the ugly spell was passed over to my young nephew Drosselmeier. Pirlipat screamed with horror at the sight of his stiff, skinny wooden body and funny big teeth and refused to marry him."

"Oh no!" exclaimed Marie.

"Now, can you guess what happened to my poor young nephew after that?" asked Godfather Drosselmeier.

Marie looked down at the Nutcracker doll in her arms and her heart swelled with love and pity. She understood that this was the young Drosselmeier who had cured Princess Pirlipat with his brave nutcracking.

"But how can we help him change back into his old self?" she wondered aloud.

"Well, the only way that will happen," explained her godfather, "is if he kills the seven-headed son of Madam Mouserinks."

"Oh! That must be the Mouse King!" exclaimed Marie.

"And he must win a young lady's heart, despite his ugliness."

"Don't worry, I'll help you break the spell," she whispered into the Nutcracker's wooden ear.

"Maybe I can help too," offered her godfather as he stood up to go. "I can build you a mousetrap. They're not hard to make."

But in the end, the Nutcracker didn't need a mousetrap at all. Before she went to bed that night, Marie handed him a gleaming sword borrowed from one of Fritz's toy soldiers. When she woke up the next morning, the Nutcracker was alive again—just like the night of the Christmas party.

"I did it!" he announced proudly, kneeling down before her in gratitude as he returned the sword, along with the defeated Mouse King's seven golden crowns. "And it's all thanks to you, my dear Marie! Your love gave me the strength I needed to fight that awful Mouse King. I can't tell you how thankful I am. So now come with me and see what splendid things I can show you."

What happened next was really and truly amazing. To celebrate, the Nutcracker took Marie on a trip to the beautiful Land of Dolls. What a lucky girl she was to visit such a place!

When they arrived, the sun was shining, beautiful music was playing, and hundreds of little sugar dolls were dancing about. Marie watched them in wonder as she and the Nutcracker strolled past the gurgling, splashing Lemonade River. Her eyes widened at the sight of the sprawling Candy Meadow, made entirely of sugary treats. But what really took her breath away was the charming little Gingerbread City made of delicious cookie houses. There, fountains of soda pop bubbled and flowed, statues carved out of cake stood in the streets, and beautifully dressed people in costumes from all over the world walked here and there, seemingly without a care in the world. In fact, everyone was smiling like it was the happiest day of their lives. Even in the most beautiful of her many picture books, Marie had never seen anything like this before!

And then the Nutcracker took her hand and led her into a little boat. Together, they sailed across a small ocean to Candy Town, with its beautiful Marzipan Castle. There he gathered a group of dolls together and told them the story of how Marie's love had saved his life. Her head swimming with happiness, she closed her eyes and listened to his gentle voice. And the more she listened, the softer and fainter his words became until ...

POOF! PLOP!

Marie opened her eyes and glanced around in surprise. Gone were the dolls and the candy fields and the cookie houses. Gone were the soda pop fountains and the Marzipan Castle. She was back in her room, lying in her own bed. And there was her own mother, pulling back the curtains and letting in the morning light.

"Nutcracker must have brought me home while I slept," she said, sitting up in bed.

"Oh, Mother dear!" she cried out. "You wouldn't believe the things I've seen!"

Marie was brimming with excitement as the story tumbled out. She told her mother about Princess Pirlipat and the Krakatuk nut and how the Nutcracker had been placed under an ugly spell. And she told her mother how he defeated the Mouse King and took her to the incredibly delicious Land of Dolls.

"Well, what a beautiful dream you had, Marie," said her mother with a little laugh as she walked out the door. "Now please get dressed. We have a guest coming today."

But you and I know that it wasn't a dream at all. And Marie knew it too. Throwing off her blanket, she jumped out of bed and ran to the toy cabinet. There she found her beloved Nutcracker, standing stiffly among the other toys.

"I'll never, ever leave you because you're ugly!" she vowed, sweeping him up in her arms. "Princess Pirlipat didn't know what a good thing she was giving up!"

And in that very instant, the ugly spell was broken.

"Marie, you're not dressed yet?" scolded her mother, who had suddenly appeared beside her. "Your godfather's young nephew from Nuremberg will be arriving any moment and you're still wearing your nightgown. Goodness! What will he say?"

Marie ran to put on her best dress, her heart dancing with joy when she heard who was coming. And when Godfather Drosselmeier's nephew finally arrived with his familiar sad smile and soldier's coat, she knew she had been right all along.

"Oh, Nutcracker! You're all better now," she whispered, her cheeks turning red at the sight of his handsome face.

As the years passed, they came to know each other very well. And then, one day, when both had grown up, he asked her to marry him. Of course she said yes, and they happily lived out the rest of their lives in the Marzipan Castle as King and Queen of the Land of Dolls.

And that's the story of the Nutcracker and the Mouse King.

THE END

Did you like that story? Would you like to see how well you remember it! Let's see if you can answer this question.

What was the name of Marie's big brother?

Was it Chips?

Was it Bits?

Was it Ditz?

Was it Fritz?

It was Fritz! Good for you! Let's try another one.

Where did the Nutcracker and Marie travel?

Was it Lemonade Land?

Was it Lollipop Land?

Was it the Land of Flowers?

Was it the Land of Dolls?

Of course, it was the Land of Dolls. Now it's time to turn out the light and dream of that beautiful place with the Gingerbread City, the Candy Meadow, and the Lemonade River. Good night.

For more Quizmas trivia questions on this story, see page 146.

The Story of
St. Nicholas

Do you like secrets? I thought so. And do you like presents?
So do I!
Well, tonight we're going to read about a magical man
who loved giving out secret presents, especially to children.
But first, let's see if you can answer this question.

Your Quizmas Question

Where does Santa Claus like to put presents?
Does he put them in the closet?
Does he put them in your mittens?
Does he hide them in your drawer?
Does he put them in your stocking?

Let's turn the page for the answer.

Your Quizmas Answer

That's right! If you hang up a stocking on Christmas Eve, Santa
Claus will come and leave presents inside. If you've
been good all year, you might find chocolates, candy,
or even a small toy or two. But if you've been naughty,
you may find a lump of coal instead.

Now did you ever wonder why Santa started putting presents
inside stockings? Or why he wears red clothes? Or where he was
born and what his real name was? Well, here's a story that will
answer all those questions. It all began a long time ago with a
young boy named Nicholas. Let's read about him now.

*O*nce upon a time, many, many, *many* years ago, a very special child was born. His name was Nicholas, and he grew up in a beautiful faraway land.

This land had rolling hills and blue skies filled with clouds of great birds. This land had tall, rugged mountains where leopards and tigers roared and roamed. And this land had deep green valleys where herds of fat wooly sheep grazed on juicy grass. This land also had mighty rivers, fine sandy beaches, and two vast seas of blue water all around it, where dolphins, seals, and turtles splashed through the salty waves.

Indeed, it was a lovely place to live, and Nicholas spent his childhood in a big house surrounded by many beautiful things. But those beautiful things never made him very happy. You see, right from the start Nicholas was different from the other children. While they were loud and rambunctious, Nicholas was gentle and calm. While they loved to get new toys for their birthdays, Nicholas liked to give his toys away. And while other children dreamed of one day being a sailor or a doctor or a great athlete, Nicholas instead dreamed of helping as many people as he could.

Yes, Nicholas was a very extraordinary boy who would grow up to be a very extraordinary man. It came as no surprise to those who knew him that he became a priest and then a bishop of the church, which was quite an important job. Nicholas dressed in the flowing red robes of a bishop, and over the years he grew a long white beard that fell from his chin like fluffy fresh winter snow. People all across this faraway land soon learned to love him for his kindness, his generosity, and his fondness for children. But what *really* made him famous was his reputation for giving secret gifts. Here's how it all started.

One day, Nicholas was working in his church when a friend came in to tell him a sad story.

"I've just met the most unlucky man," the friend said with a shake of his head. "His name is John, and only a year ago he was a rich man with a fine house and his own little shop. He also had a long list of future husbands lined up for his three beautiful daughters. I'm sure you know them. Gabrielle, the oldest daughter, plays the harp and has the prettiest singing voice in the land. Catherine, the middle daughter, is as smart as a whip and makes everybody around her laugh with her funny stories. And Christina, the youngest daughter, is as sweet as sugar and as pretty as a princess."

"Yes, I have seen them in church and they are lovely girls," said Nicholas. "So why is John so unlucky?"

His friend sighed and asked, "Do you remember the great

ship that was lost at sea last year? The one that was returning from the East carrying silk and spices?"

"Of course," the bishop said. "It was a sad time for everyone. I visited all the families of the crew."

"Well," said his friend, "what you perhaps did not know was that John owned that ship. He lost all his money when it sank. Now he and his three daughters have almost nothing left. They've been forced to move from their fine house to the most run-down little shack you've ever seen."

"How awful!" said Nicholas, who was always troubled when he heard about people living in poverty.

"Yes, but what makes the story even sadder is that his daughters, Gabrielle, Catherine, and Christina, will grow old alone, for without a dowry, who will ever marry them?"

A dowry, you see, was a certain amount of money that every girl needed to get married in that long-ago time.

"Oh, those poor girls!" said Nicholas sadly. "That means they will never have children, and John will never know the joys of being a grandfather."

"Yes," agreed his friend. "I've heard that John is so worried about them, he cries himself to sleep every single night. Oh, Bishop Nicholas, I've come to you with their story in the hope that you might be able to help somehow."

Nicholas promised he would do all he could. And so, after his friend left, he spent a long time thinking about poor, unlucky John and his three daughters. For many hours, he twirled his fingers around and around the tip of his fluffy white beard and wondered what to do. Finally, he had an idea.

As soon as night fell, he grabbed his pack and set out on his horse to find the poor man's shack. Luckily, the moon was almost full, which made it easy for Nicholas to find his way in the dark. After searching for a while, he finally came across the most run-down little house he'd ever seen. Standing in the middle of an overgrown field, it had paper-thin walls, a crumbling chimney, and two tiny, cracked windows.

"This must be the place," thought Nicholas as he crept over to the first window and peeked inside. In the moonlight he could see three young girls sleeping, huddled together on a lumpy mattress with only a thin, worn blanket to cover them. Nicholas had no doubt that he'd found Gabrielle, Catherine, and Christina, for they were just as beautiful as he remembered. Their long, flowing dark hair fanned out around their heads like halos, and their sleeping faces were as lovely as newly opened roses.

"I've come to help you girls," he whispered tenderly. Then, as quietly as possible, he crept over to the other window and looked inside. What he saw filled him with sadness. The walls were bare and peeling and not a stick of furniture was to be found. And there was poor, unlucky John asleep on the floor by the fireplace where his daughters' tattered stockings and skirts were hanging to dry. He was shivering, for the fire was almost out and there were no more logs to heat the house. Nicholas could see that the tears were still fresh on his cheeks from crying himself to sleep.

Nicholas's kind heart ached at the sight of this poor family. Doing his best not to wake anyone up, he reached into his pack and pulled out a small bag of solid gold coins. Then, heaving the bag up onto his shoulder, he tossed it through the crack in the window. It sailed through the air and—*PLOP!*—landed right in one of the hanging stockings. Nicholas smiled to himself, ran back to his horse, and rode away through the darkness.

The next morning, when the three girls woke up, they went to the fireplace to see if their clothes were dry.

"Look, Gabrielle!" said the youngest sister to the oldest. "There's something inside one of your stockings!" Gabrielle frowned with confusion, took her stocking down from the fireplace, and reached her hand inside to see what it was. Imagine her shock and surprise when she pulled out the bag of gold coins!

For a moment she didn't know what to say. Then, yelping with joy, she ran to wake up her father with kisses and hugs and cries of delight. The poor little run-down shack was suddenly alive with happiness.

"Oh, Father dear! Look and see what has happened!" she squealed, as her sisters gathered around her to *ooh* and *aah* over the gold. "It's a miracle! All our prayers have been answered!"

With trembling hands, John emptied the little bag out onto the floor, and slowly he and his daughters began counting the coins. They counted them not just once, not just twice, but three times, as if they expected the gold to somehow start disappearing just as mysteriously as it had appeared. When they finally finished counting, they jumped up and down with delight, for it was a small fortune—more than enough for Gabrielle's dowry.

Needless to say, John was absolutely thrilled that at least one of his daughters could now marry. And yet for the rest of that day, a question burned at the back of his mind. Who could have given them such a gift?

Of course, he had no way of knowing what was going to happen next. You see, later that same day, after the sun had set and the moon and stars had come out, Nicholas secretly returned on his horse to the little shack in the field. In his pack, he brought with him another bag of gold, this one for the middle daughter.

Then, just as he'd done the night before, he checked to make sure everyone was sleeping, heaved the bag up onto his shoulder, and tossed it through the crack in the window. *PLOP!* It landed right in another stocking!

When Catherine woke the next morning to find the bag of gold in her stocking, she clapped her hands and hopped up and down with glee.

"Father, Father! It's happened again! Look what I found in *my* stocking!" she cried out as her beautiful face lit up with joy. "Now I can get married too!"

Gabrielle and Christina gathered her up in their arms, and together the three sisters began to dance around the little shack. Their father was pleased to see his daughters so happy, and yet he didn't join them in their dance. Instead, he scratched his forehead and frowned, for he was very confused. Even back when he was a rich man, he didn't know anybody generous enough to give gifts such as these.

"Who on earth could be so kind as to give us *two* bags of gold?" he wondered as he watched Gabrielle, Catherine, and little Christina dance. And suddenly he had an idea of how he might solve the mystery.

"*Two* bags of gold on *two* nights for *two* daughters," thought John with the satisfaction of a detective about to crack his case, "but I still have *one* daughter left! Maybe this secret gift-giver will come again."

The next night was cloudy and dark. After his girls had hung up their clothes by the fireplace, John gave them each a kiss and sent them off to bed. Then he settled down on the cold, hard floor to wait. For several hours he lay there listening for noises, watching in the darkness, and waiting to see if someone would appear with one more bag of gold for his last daughter, pretty little Christina.

The evening hours ticked by slowly. So slowly, in fact, that John was almost asleep when Nicholas arrived on his horse. Almost asleep, but not quite! Suddenly, a bag of gold sailed through the window. *PLOP!* It landed right in Christina's stocking.

John jumped to his feet and ran to the window. He got there just in time to see a man with a white beard riding away on his horse.

"Stop, stop! Show me your face!" John yelled out after him. "Please! I want to thank you for what you've done!"

But the horse and rider paid no attention to his calls and galloped away into the shadows. Then, just before they rode out of sight, the clouds cleared and a patch of moonlight lit up the rider's bright red robe.

"Heavens above! That could be only one man," John said to himself. "It must be Bishop Nicholas!"

Brimming with excitement, he ran to wake up his daughters and tell them what he had just seen. And they, in turn, told all of their friends about Nicholas's kind gifts. Soon word of the bishop's generosity spread across the land, and before long, children everywhere began to dream of getting a visit from Nicholas. They would hang their stockings by the fireplace on wintry nights, hoping they too might wake up to find them filled with gifts. And often they did. In fact, I'll bet you'll be doing that too a few nights from now.

You see, although Nicholas lived so many years ago, the world has never forgotten what a generous and loving person he was. He was even made into a saint, which is a title for only the holiest of people. Even though hundreds and hundreds of years have passed, his spirit is still very much alive today in the jolly old soul we welcome into our homes each Christmas.

That's right—St. Nicholas, the kind man with the long white beard and red clothes who loved children and giving gifts, was the same man who would one day become known as Santa Claus.

And so, little children, when you hang up your stocking by the fireplace this Christmas Eve, remember good old St. Nicholas and the story you just heard.

And think about his gentle heart with every gift that you receive.

And know you are carrying on his life's work with every gift that you give.

The End
〜

Did you like that story? Would you like to see how well you remember it? Let's see if you can answer this question.

What did Nicholas become when he grew up?

Did he become a doctor?

Did he become a sailor?

Did he become an athlete?

Did he become a bishop?

He became a bishop. Very good! Let's try another one.

What kind of gift did Nicholas leave for the three poor daughters?

Did he leave candy canes?

Did he leave dolls?

Did he leave new clothes?

Did he leave bags of gold?

That's right, he left three bags of gold. I hope you enjoyed the story of how a long-ago man called St. Nicholas became the Santa Claus we know and love today. Now you'd better get to bed, because I think he'll be visiting our house very soon. Good night.

For more Quizmas trivia questions on this story,
see page 150.

For more Quizmas trivia questions on this story, see page 150.

A Journey to
Santa's Castle

Tonight, we're going to read our last story. But before we start, see if you know the answer to this question.

Your Quizmas Question

Where does Santa Claus live?
Does he live in the refrigerator?
Does he live in Florida?
Does he live at the South Pole?
Does he live at the North Pole?

Let's turn the page and find out.

Your Quizmas Answer

That's right. Santa Claus lives at the North Pole,
in a beautiful castle surrounded by snow.
But did you ever wonder what his workshop looks like?
Or where the reindeer sleep? Or where Santa keeps his sleigh?
Or what kind of cookies are his favorites? Well, here's a story
that will explain it all. Let's read it together now.

*K*elly was a little kid just about your age. She had a long brown ponytail and big blue eyes. She had freckles on her nose and big, round, rosy cheeks—the kind of cheeks that grown-ups just love to pinch. Kelly liked to go swimming in the summer and sledding and ice skating in the winter. Every fall, she liked dressing up in scary costumes for Halloween. And each spring, she liked looking for eggs on Easter morning.

But the one holiday that Kelly really, really, *really* loved above all the others was Christmas. She loved decorating the tree, she loved eating the turkey dinner, she loved opening the presents, and most of all she loved Santa Claus. She loved him so much that she often thought about him even after Christmas morning had come and gone and the decorations had been put away in their boxes for another year.

"Mommy, how does Santa see me when I'm sleeping?" Kelly asked one summer evening as she was being tucked into bed.

"Well, he's magic of course!" replied her mother, leaning over to give her a good-night kiss. Kelly thought about this for a moment.

"Is that why he can make *so* many toys for *so* many of us kids?"

Her mother nodded. "Yes. And remember, he also has a team of elves helping him in his workshop."

"Oh, that's right," Kelly said with a smile. "And where's his workshop, Mommy?"

"Why, it's at the North Pole, of course," her mother replied, snapping off the light, "inside Santa's castle."

"Okay, so where's the North Pole?" asked Kelly.

Kelly's mother made a funny face, the kind she sometimes made when Kelly asked too many questions. "It's the coldest and snowiest place on earth, all the way at the top of the world. If you followed a compass north and just kept walking, you'd eventually find it," she whispered, pulling the door shut. "Now go to sleep."

Well, that was easier said than done. You see, her mother had planted a brilliant idea in Kelly's ponytailed head. For the rest of the night, all she could do was think about heading north and finding Santa Claus's castle and meeting him in person. She had a compass, after all—she'd found one in a Christmas cracker the previous December and had kept it in her top drawer ever since.

And so early the next morning, she packed her backpack with some cookies, a hat, and her warmest mittens. And then she grabbed her compass and placed a little note on her pillow that read: *Gone to the North Pole.*

And then Kelly set off to find Santa Claus.

She walked for weeks and weeks and weeks and weeks, always checking the compass to make sure her feet were pointed north.

She walked through big cities and little towns.

She walked through thick forests of evergreens.

She walked across vast open fields of tall grass.

When her feet got tired, she'd sit and rest for a little while. And when she felt better, she'd get up and walk some more.

Finally, after walking more miles than she knew how to count, the air grew colder and the ground gradually became white with ice and snow. This made Kelly very happy because she knew it meant she was finally getting close to the North Pole. And the colder and snowier it got, the more exited Kelly became.

Suddenly, *WHOOOOOOOOOOOOOSH!*

A blast of icy wind came rushing by, stirring up clouds of snow into a frosty whirlwind and landing with a frozen kiss on Kelly's big, round, rosy cheeks. Reaching into her backpack, she put on her mittens and hat and pressed on through the wind, certain she was almost there.

And she was right. Minutes later, she spotted the four turrets of a castle. They rose up above the snowdrifts like the peaks of a lemon meringue pie. At the top of each turret was a golden Christmas star, shining brightly in the dark, frozen sky.

"There it is! It's Santa's castle! I found it, I found it!" she squealed, jumping up and down with glee.

Her heart racing with excitement, Kelly hurried over the snowdrifts and across the fields of crackling ice until she could see the entire castle. The sight of it nearly stole her frozen breath away. It was almost too beautiful to be real, like something you would see in a dream!

The castle was a glistening vision of frosted blue ice, so big and grand that Kelly was certain it could contain a small town. The two enormous front doors were carved out of thick glacier ice, and all the windows were made of colorful stained glass. A forest of Christmas trees decorated with lights and tinsel and ornaments encircled the castle.

Kelly hurried up to the gleaming icicle gate that surrounded the property. There she came upon a pair of snowmen standing guard. One was tall with skinny stick arms that stuck out from his body, while the other one was short and round and had stubby snow hands.

"Stop! Who goes there?" asked the first snowman, with a tilt of his silky top hat.

Kelly was a little bit surprised and a little bit afraid. She'd never heard a snowman talk before.

"H-h-h-hi. My name's Kelly. I've come to see Santa Claus. Can … can I come in?"

"Well, that depends," said the other snowman, peering down

from his post with his coal black eyes. "Have you been naughty, or nice?"

"Oh, I'm definitely nice, Sir Snowman," replied Kelly quickly "I help with my baby brother, I keep my room clean, and I always listen to my parents."

Hearing this, the two snowmen's button mouths broke into wide smiles.

"Well then, you can come in!" said the first snowman. "We'll let Santa know that another child is here to visit."

"*Another* child?" asked Kelly, looking confused.

The second snowman laughed from deep inside his round snow belly. "Of course! You don't think you're the first one to ever come looking for Santa Claus, do you?"

And with that, the icicle gate swung open. Clutching her backpack, Kelly walked timidly up to the castle, through the enormous glacier doors, and into the front room. A blast of warm air greeted her like a friendly hug, bringing feeling back to her chilly nose, cheeks, fingers, and toes.

"I'll be back in a jiffy," promised the tall snowman as he glided off to find Santa. While she waited for him to return, Kelly pulled off her hat and gazed around the room in wonder. Even though it was August, the entire place looked and smelled like Christmas. The walls were decorated with mistletoe and holly and ribboned wreaths of evergreen boughs. Strings of garland and tinsel hung from the high ceiling, which was painted to look like the night sky.

Suddenly, a deep and joyful "ho ho ho" rang out from behind her. With a squeal of delight, Kelly spun around and came face to face with Santa Claus himself!

"Hello there, Kelly!" he chuckled, reaching out to greet her with a big hug.

"Santa!" she cried out, dropping her backpack and running to his side. She threw her little arms around his big, round body and squeezed him tight. His red suit was soft and velvety and warm, and the fur trim on his collar tickled her cheeks and made her laugh. She closed her eyes and took a deep breath.

"Mmmmm. Santa, you smell like a candy cane," she whispered in his ear.

Santa laughed again and patted her on the head.

"How was your journey?" he asked. "I've been expecting you for several weeks now."

"Y-y-you knew I was coming?" she gasped in amazement.

"My dear, have you forgotten that I can see you when you're sleeping?" he asked with a playful wink.

Kelly smiled bashfully and nodded her head. "Yes, I guess I did forget."

"All right, Kelly," said Santa, suddenly sounding serious. "Now that you've come so far, tell me what I can do for you."

"Well, I-I-I'd love to come in for a while and look around your castle," she answered hopefully, "and maybe meet Mrs. Claus, too."

"I think that sounds like a fine idea!" Santa replied, smiling his merry smile. "Come along with me and I'll give you the grand tour!"

Taking her little mittened hand in his big one, Santa led her down a very long hallway. After walking for many minutes, they came upon a row of doors. Santa stopped in front of the first one and said, "Let's start here."

Kelly nodded her head eagerly. There were some awfully loud noises coming from inside that room and she was terribly curious as to what they might be. The noises sounded like this:

BANG-POUND-WHACK-POUND-RATTLE-BANG-WHUMP!

Santa waved his hand and the door magically swung open, revealing a room so large it could have held a whole football field. Stepping inside, Kelly looked around in amazement, for it truly was a wondrous sight to behold! Hundreds and hundreds of little elves were hard at work at their little benches, hammering and painting and putting together hundreds and hundreds of toys. This one was making a doll, that one was building a train set, and that one over there was finishing up a jigsaw puzzle. It was Santa's workshop!

"So that's how you make *so* many toys," Kelly whispered under her breath, her eyes just about popping out of her head at the sight.

Almost as incredible as all the toys were the elves themselves! They were so tiny, and each one was dressed in a little leafy green outfit with a red cap and pointed shoes with bells on the tips of each toe.

The elves stopped for only the briefest of moments when Santa and Kelly walked in the door, then quickly got back to their toys, singing all the while:

> Work, work, work, all through the year,
> For Christmas day is drawing near.
> A bear for Dahlia and a puppet for Elaine,
> Hailey wants a car and Jonah wants a train.
> Work, work, work, to make these toys,
> For all those good little girls and boys.

"I think we should move on now, Kelly," suggested Santa, guiding her out with a gentle nudge. "There's still so much for you to see."

Together they walked down the hallway to the next room, where, just like before, Kelly heard strange sounds coming from behind the door. But this time the sounds were much softer, kind of like this:

Shuffle … jingle, jingle … shuffle … jingle, jingle … shuffle

Before she had the chance to ask Santa what was going on, he opened the door and explained, "This is my mail room. It's the place where all the letters you children send me are opened. We have a very organized system here—each letter is read and then sorted according to the child's country and level of kindness."

Kelly poked her head inside the room and was surprised to see more elves hard at work, the bells on their toes jingling merrily as they ran back and forth fetching letters from the heaps of overflowing mailbags piled up on the floor.

"Gosh, Santa, I didn't know your elves had other jobs."

"Oh yes," boasted Santa proudly. "My elves run this castle like a well-fed reindeer. Come along and I'll show you what else they do around here."

Santa put a hand on Kelly's shoulder and guided her down the hall to the next room, where a loud buzzing noise could be heard as they got closer.

WHIR … WHIR … WHIRRRRRRRRRRRR … WHIR!

Kelly took a timid step back. It sounded like there might be a hive of angry bees in that room! Before she had the chance to ask what it was, the door opened and Santa led her inside. She looked around and saw more elves, all of them seated in front of teeny tiny sewing machines. They were busily working away with heaps of red and green material piled up at their feet.

"What are they doing?" she asked, speaking loudly to make her voice heard above the whirring.

"Ho ho ho," chuckled Santa. "This is the castle's sewing room. These elves work all year long fixing up holes in toes and stitching together new stockings for kids around the world. In fact, Kelly, I believe your stocking was here a few weeks ago for repair."

"You're right! It did have a hole!" she gasped, peering around the room to see if she could spot it. But there was so much going on, and it was next to impossible to tell one stocking from the other. Those elves looked so adorable sitting at their little sewing machines that Kelly wondered if she would be allowed to walk over and give one of them a hug. But the next thing she knew, Santa was tugging on her sleeve and pulling her out the door.

"Come along now. The next stop on the tour is my personal favorite," he said proudly as he showed her to the next room.

Squeak … splash … squeak … splash … squeak … splash

The sounds came from behind another closed door. Kelly held her breath and waited for Santa to open it. She couldn't even imagine what was making all those funny noises. Could it be a mouse swimming-pool party? Or maybe an underwater hamster wheel? A moment later, the answer was revealed.

"Here is the maintenance shop," Santa announced, opening the door with another wave of his hand. "This is where my sleigh is repaired and put into top shape for the big Christmas Eve trip."

"Wow!" Kelly chirped, clapping her hands with excitement as they entered, for in front of her sat Santa's famous sleigh, so big she could hardly take it all in! The body of the sleigh was painted in the brightest shade of Christmas red, and its shiny silver runners gleamed with light. An army of little elves was busily scrubbing away at the sleigh with wet sponges and buckets of soapy water.

Squeak ... splash ... squeak ... splash ... squeak ... splash went the sponges as they worked to clean the sleigh.

Kelly took a timid step closer and saw that the seats inside were covered in cozy white fur blankets. She longed to walk over and touch them, but didn't know if she dared ask.

"My little elves keep it shined up and in tip-top shape all year round," explained Santa, patting the side of the sleigh lovingly. "Go on and climb aboard if you'd like," he added, as if reading her mind. "I'm sure you'll find it very comfortable."

And so with a little boost from St. Nick himself, Kelly scrambled up over the elves' heads and into the sleigh.

"Gosh! I can't believe I'm actually sitting in Santa's sleigh!" she gasped, running her hands over the soft furry seats. She closed her eyes for a moment and smiled, trying to imagine what it might be like to be pulled by a team of reindeer across the cold December sky.

She sat in that sleigh for the longest time, thinking to herself that she was the luckiest child in the entire world. But as much as Kelly would have liked to stay there forever, she climbed down when Santa Claus announced that it was time to move on.

"It's getting late and there's more to see," he said, motioning for her to follow him back into the hallway. They walked together for quite a while before arriving at the next room, where, just like before, Kelly heard strange noises rolling out from the crack under the door. Only these noises sounded a bit more familiar— almost like a chorus of loud snoring.

Zzzzzz ... zzzzzz ... zzzzzz ... zzzzzz ... zzzzzz

"Now, before we go in, please promise me you'll be very quiet," said Santa in a hushed voice.

"Okay, I promise!" Kelly quickly agreed.

A moment later, the door opened and a strange smell wafted up to Kelly's nose. It took her a couple of seconds to realize that it was the smell of fresh hay. She peeked around the doorway and saw that inside was a very large stable. Then she saw them—eight beautiful reindeer lying on eight beautiful red velvet beds, each with a hand-painted nameplate hanging on a golden chain above the stall. They were, of course, Dasher, Dancer, Prancer, Vixen, Comet, Cupid, Donder, and Blitzen. And they were all sound asleep!

"Oh! Is this where they live?" she blurted out, forgetting her promise to be quiet. At the sound of her voice, Comet stopped snoring, lifted his antlered head off his pillow, and looked around.

"Shhhh. Yes, but they sleep all year," whispered Santa, holding a finger up to his lips. "They need a lot of rest to get ready for their big flight on Christmas Eve."

Spotting his master, Comet gave a contented snort and rose to his feet.

"Uh-oh. Let's go now, before we wake up any more of them," said Santa, turning to leave.

"But … but …," protested Kelly. She was secretly hoping to stay and pat the reindeer and maybe even feed one of them. But she followed Santa out of the stable. After all, what child in the world is going to argue with Santa Claus?

"Come now, Kelly," he said as they made their way back down the long hallway. "There's just one more thing I want to show you before we're done with the tour."

A few minutes later they arrived at a pair of double doors decorated with two giant Christmas wreaths. "This is the part of the castle where I live," Santa explained, holding the doors open for her as she walked inside and looked around.

The room was long and wide and yet somehow still cozy. It had high ceilings and vast picture windows that offered a beautiful view of the giant snowdrifts outside. On one side of the room was a majestic Christmas tree, so tall that it reached all the way up to the ceiling. On the other side of the room was a big stone fireplace with a crackling fire. Decorating the walls in between were pages and pages and pages of children's artwork, their bright colors covering every spare inch of space.

Still feeling a bit cold, Kelly walked over to the fire to warm up her hands. A moment later, she was greeted by a kind-looking lady with smiling dimples, a long salt-and-pepper braid, and a roly-poly tummy, almost as big and round as Santa's. It was, of course, Mrs. Claus!

"Hello, dear," she said, holding open her soft arms and wrapping Kelly up into a big hug. Kelly breathed deeply. "Mmmmm … and you smell like gingerbread," she said with a smile. Mrs. Claus laughed at this and then pinched Kelly's round, rosy cheeks.

"Goodness, you still feel chilly!" she clucked. "Let's get you something to eat. You must be very hungry from your long walk."

She was indeed! In fact, the mere mention of food made her tummy start to rumble. And so, leading her over to one of two large, comfy chairs in front of the fireplace, Mrs. Claus settled Kelly with a blanket then scurried off toward the kitchen.

"I'll be right back with a cup of hot cocoa and some of my special homemade chocolate chip cookies," she called out over her shoulder.

"Those are my favorite, you know," confessed Santa, plopping himself down heavily in the chair next to Kelly. When Mrs. Claus returned with the goodies, he leaned back in his chair and watched her eat. Only once the cocoa was gone and she'd had her fill of cookies did he start asking questions.

"So, Kelly, I've been wondering, how did you find my castle anyway?"

"I pointed my compass north and just started walking, like my mother said I should," she replied, wiping the crumbs from her lips with the back of her hand.

"Oh. So does she know where you are?" he asked, raising an eyebrow.

"Yes, I … um … I … left her a note."

"I see … a note," repeated Santa with a little frown. "So you don't think she'll be worried at all?"

"Um, well … maybe a little bit," she admitted.

"Hmmm. Worrying your mother … that's not very nice, is it?" he asked, with a sad shake of his head.

Not knowing what to say to this, Kelly just stared down at her shoes. Santa was right—her mother probably *was* worried. For the first time since she left home, she began to feel a little bit guilty.

"Sorry, Santa," she whispered after a couple of minutes.

"Well, now," he said, stroking his beard thoughtfully, "maybe, just *maybe* I can think of a way to fix this problem."

"You can?" Kelly asked, lifting her gaze back up. "How?"

"Well, it's kind of tricky, but lucky for you I know a little magic," he replied with a wink.

Putting down his pipe, he picked up a small silver bell and gave it a ring. Instantly, a tiny elf appeared at his side.

"Comet's awake," Santa informed the elf. "Please have him saddled up and prepared for flight. He's going to take this little girl back home today."

Kelly's heart leapt with excitement on hearing these words. "I really get to ride Comet?" she gasped, jumping down from her chair.

"That's right," replied Santa, rising to his feet. "It's the quickest way to get you back home to your poor mother. Now let's get going."

And so, after she used the bathroom and said goodbye to Mrs. Claus, he took her hand and walked her outside where Comet was ready, saddled and waiting.

"Goodbye, Kelly," he said, lifting her up onto the reindeer's back. "Next time you want to come for a visit, remember to bring one of your parents along!"

"Goodbye, Santa! Thank you for everything," she replied, kissing his soft, bearded cheek. "See you next Christmas!"

And with that they were off! With her backpack strapped on tightly, Kelly wrapped her arms around Comet's strong neck and nestled her face against his warm fur as he took to the skies. It was the most thrilling ride of Kelly's life! They flew for many hours, all alone up there except for a few flocks of birds. The rushing of the wind and the sound of Comet's heavy, panting breath filled her ears. And up close, the brightness of the stars and moon dazzled her eyes with their brilliant light.

They flew so long, so high, so fast! By the time they finally arrived at Kelly's house she was tired out. Sliding down off

Comet's back, she gave him a pat between his antlers and then stumbled into her house, tumbled into her bed, and fell fast asleep for a very long time.

The next thing she knew, somebody was whispering in her ear.

"Honey, wake up! You've overslept!"

Kelly opened her eyes and looked up into her mother's face. Her heart swelled with love and relief.

"Oh, Mommy! I'm so sorry I worried you!" she cried, reaching up to give her a hug. "I promise I'll never run away again!"

"But what are you talking about, sweetheart?" Her mother laughed. "You've been here in your room since I tucked you into bed last night."

"No, no I haven't!" Kelly insisted with a shake of her head. "I was with Santa Claus!"

And with that, the whole story tumbled out of her, from her long walk to the North Pole, to her tour of Santa's castle, to her incredible ride home on Comet's back.

"Wow! That sounds like a very beautiful dream," said her mother with a smile.

"But no, it wasn't a dream at all …," Kelly started to say. But then she stopped as she began to realize what had *really* happened. She smiled at her mother and then never said another word about it.

But for the rest of her life, even when she grew into an old lady with wrinkles and white hair, Kelly always knew that it was Santa's magic that had turned back time and brought her back to her own bed the very same night that she had left for her long walk to the North Pole.

After all, it couldn't all have been a dream, could it?

THE END
〜

Did you like that story? Would you like to see how well you remember it? Let's see if you can answer this question.

Who helps Santa run his workshop?

Are they dwarves?

Are they fairies?

Are they elves?

Are they goblins?

That's right, they're elves! Good for you! Let's try another one.

What kind of building does Santa live in?

Does he live in a tent?

Does he live in a tepee?

Does he live in a cave?

Does he live in a castle?

You're right! Santa lives in a beautiful castle, with stained glass windows, an icicle gate, and a forest of Christmas trees. Now it's time to go to bed, because he'll be flying across the skies to visit our house very soon. Good night.

For more Quizmas trivia questions on this story,
see page 154.

Quizmas Trivia Fun

We've read many wonderful stories in this book, haven't we? Do you think you remember them?
Let's try some more questions and see.

The Nativity Story

I. **What was the name of the town Mary and Joseph were traveling to?**

Was it Nazareth?

Was it Jerusalem?

Was it Bethlehem?

Was it Jericho?

It was Bethlehem.

2. **What was about to happen to Mary?**

Was she going to eat dinner?

Was she going to ride a camel?

Was she going to sleep?

Was she going to have a baby?

She was going to have a baby.

3. What was the weather like when they arrived in Bethlehem?

Was it sunny?

Was it snowing?

Was it cloudy?

Was it cold and drizzling?

It was cold and drizzling.

4. Where did the innkeeper tell Joseph and Mary to go?

Was it to a room inside the inn?

Was it to another inn nearby?

Was it to a stable behind the inn?

Was it to another town?

It was to a stable behind the inn.

5. Who had come to Mary in a dream to tell her she would have a very special baby?

Was it Joseph?

Was it shepherds?

Was it the innkeeper?

Was it the angel Gabriel?

It was the angel Gabriel.

6. What animals were the shepherds watching over?

   Were they goats?

   Were they horses?

   Were they sheep?

   Were they cows?

   They were sheep.

7. Who did the shepherds see in the sky?

   Was it Mary?

   Was it the Baby Jesus?

   Was it Joseph?

   Was it an angel?

   It was an angel.

8. How did the shepherds feel when a bright light suddenly lit up the night sky?

   Were they excited?

   Were they happy?

   Were they frightened?

   Were they hungry?

   They were frightened.

9. What did the angel call the Baby Jesus?

Did he call him a king?

Did he call him an emperor?

Did he call him a Savior?

Did he call him a prince?

He called him a Savior.

10. What did the shepherds do after the angel appeared?

Did they go to sleep?

Did they sit by the fire?

Did they sing songs?

Did they go to see the Baby Jesus?

They went to see the Baby Jesus.

The Three Kings

1. What country did Balthasar rule over?

   Was it the United States?

   Was it England?

   Was it Canada?

   Was it Ethiopia?

   It was Ethiopia.

2. Which animals could Balthasar see from his palace?

   Were they dolphins and whales?

   Were they zebras and giraffes?

   Were they rabbits and squirrels?

   Were they dogs and cats?

   Yes, they were zebras and giraffes.

3. **What animal roars loudly?**

Is it a billy goat?

Is it a mouse?

Is it a chipmunk?

Is it a lion?

Of course, it is a lion.

4. **What did Balthasar ride when he left his country?**

Was it an elephant?

Was it a gazelle?

Was it a hippo?

Was it a horse?

It was a horse.

5. **What gift did Balthasar decide to bring to the Baby Jesus?**

Was it a great diamond?

Was it a caged lion?

Was it a parrot?

Was it myrrh?

Yes, it was myrrh.

6. **Where did Melchior live?**

Did he live in a house?

Did he live in a tent?

Did he live in a castle?

Did he live in a boat?

He lived in a tent.

7. **What was there a lot of in Arabia?**

Was it water?

Was it snow?

Was it sand?

Was it grass?

It was sand.

8. **What animal was Melchior riding?**

Was it a donkey?

Was it a zebra?

Was it an ostrich?

Was it a camel?

It was a camel.

9. How did Gaspar travel as he followed the star?

   Was he on a train?

   Was he on a plane?

   Was he in a car?

   Was he on a ship?

   He was on a ship.

10. Whom did the Three Kings visit before they went to Bethlehem?

    Was it an angel?

    Was it shepherds?

    Was it King Herod?

    Was it a wizard?

    It was King Herod.

The Christmas Animals

I. What color was the little donkey?

Was he black?

Was he gray?

Was he pink?

Was he brown?

Yes, he was brown.

2. What color were the little donkey's eyes?

Were they blue?

Were they green?

Were they gray?

Were they brown?

They were brown.

3. What woke the little donkey at midnight?

   Was it the rooster crowing?

   Was it the cow mooing?

   Was it the nightingale singing?

   Was it a bright light?

   Yes, it was a bright light that filled the stable.

4. What did all the animals do to honor the Baby Jesus?

   Did they dance?

   Did they sing?

   Did they bow down?

   Did they bring gifts?

   That's right, they bowed down.

5. Which bird fanned the fire with its wings?

   Was it the stork?

   Was it the rooster?

   Was it the nightingale?

   Was it the robin?

   It was the robin.

6. Which bird said it would fly to the rooftop and tell the world about the birth of Jesus?

Was it the hen?

Was it the rooster?

Was it the robin?

Was it the nightingale?

Yes, it was the rooster.

7. Who said they would all hum praises to Jesus together?

Was it the sheep?

Was it the bees?

Was it the hens?

Was it the cows?

Yes, it was the bees.

8. What was the biggest bird in the stable that night?

Was it the robin?

Was it the rooster?

Was it the stork?

Was it the nightingale?

That's right, it was the stork.

9. **What was the Baby Jesus lying on in the manger?**

   Was it sand?

   Was it snow?

   Was it grass?

   Was it straw?

   It was straw.

10. **What gift did the stork give to the Baby Jesus?**

    Was it eggs?

    Was it a song?

    Was it her feathers?

    Was it her nest?

    It was her soft feathers.

A Christmas Carol

I. Which merry holiday did Ebenezer Scrooge dislike?

Was it Easter?

Was it Valentine's Day?

Was it Halloween?

Was it Christmas?

It was Christmas.

2. What funny expression was Ebenezer Scrooge often heard saying?

Was it "blah crumbug"?

Was it "boo bumlug"?

Was it "bah humbug"?

Was it "bo drumhug"?

It was "bah humbug."

3. What was the name of Scrooge's clerk?

Was it Bill Rachit?

Was it Brian Matchit?

Was it Brad Patchit?

Was it Bob Cratchit?

It was Bob Cratchit.

4. What was the weather like when Ebenezer Scrooge trudged home on Christmas Eve?

Was it rainy?

Was it snowy?

Was it windy?

Was it sunny?

It was snowy.

5. Who did Ebenezer Scrooge live with in his big, empty, cold, dark house?

Was it his mother?

Was it his grandpa?

Was it his cousin?

Did he live all alone?

He lived all alone.

6. **What was the ghost of Jacob Marley wearing when he came to visit Scrooge?**

   Was it a fuzzy scarf?

   Was it a long chain?

   Was it a silly hat?

   Was it pajamas?

   It was a long chain.

7. **What sound did Jacob Marley's chains make when they rattled?**

   Was it *ding ... dong ... ding*?

   Was it *ho-ho-ho*?

   Was it *slurp ... slurp ... slurp*?

   Was it *KA-CHUNK—KA-CHINK—KA-CHUNK*?

   It was KA-CHUNK—KA-CHINK—KA-CHUNK.

8. **How many ghosts did Marley send to visit Scrooge?**

   Was it one ghost?

   Was it three ghosts?

   Was it ten ghosts?

   Was it a hundred ghosts?

   It was three ghosts.

9. What was the name of the first ghost to visit Scrooge?

Was it Harry?

Was it Randall?

Was it Peter?

Was it the Ghost of Christmas Past?

It was the Ghost of Christmas Past.

10. What did Scrooge buy for the Cratchits' Christmas dinner?

Was it a big turkey?

Was it a goose?

Was it a chicken?

Was it a rooster?

It was a big turkey.

The Nutcracker

I. What was the name of Marie and Fritz's godfather?

Was it Frankenstein?

Was it Superman?

Was it Dracula?

Was it Drosselmeier?

It was Drosselmeier.

2. What kind of toys did Fritz like to play with?

Were they toy soldiers?

Were they electric trains?

Were they teddy bears?

Were they puzzles?

Fritz liked to play with toy soldiers.

3. **What kind of present did Godfather Drosselmeier make for Marie and Fritz?**

Was it a pair of new bicycles?

Was it a remote-control car?

Was it a beautiful wooden castle?

Was it a package of new crayons?

It was a beautiful wooden castle.

4. **What color coat was the Nutcracker wearing?**

Was it pink?

Was it violet with white braid?

Was it black?

Was it red with gold trim?

It was violet with white braid.

5. **Who did the Nutcracker fight with?**

Was it the Sugar Plum Fairy?

Was it the Mouse King?

Was it toy soldiers?

Was it dolls?

Yes, it was the Mouse King.

6. How many heads did the Mouse King have?

Did he have one?

Did he have two?

Did he have seven?

Did he have none?

He had seven heads.

7. What did Marie throw at the mice to try to save her Nutcracker doll?

Was it a book?

Was it a candy cane?

Was it her slipper?

Was it a Christmas ornament?

She threw her slipper.

8. Who put a spell on Princess Pirlipat?

Was it Master Mumfred?

Was it Monsieur Marble?

Was it Mademoiselle Marmalade?

Was it Madam Mouserinks?

It was Madam Mouserinks.

9. In the story, what was the name of the hardest nut in the entire world?

Was it Bricknut?

Was it Toughnut?

Was it Krakatuk?

Was it Marshmallow?

It was Krakatuk.

10. In the end, who did the Nutcracker turn out to be?

Was he Marie's schoolteacher?

Was he Godfather Drosselmeier's nephew?

Was he the Mouse King's brother?

Was he Princess Pirlipat's baby sister?

He was Godfather Drosselmeier's nephew.

The Story of St. Nicholas

1. When was Nicholas born?

   Was he born yesterday?

   Was he born last week?

   Was he born last year?

   Was he born many, many, many years ago?

   Nicholas was born many, many, many years ago.

2. What color were Nicholas's robes?

   Were they blue?

   Were they green?

   Were they yellow?

   Were they red?

   They were red.

3. **Where did Nicholas work?**

Did he work in a school?

Did he work in a store?

Did he work in a church?

Did he work in a bank?

Nicholas worked in a church.

4. **How many daughters did poor, unlucky John have?**

Did he have one daughter?

Did he have two daughters?

Did he have three daughters?

Did he have no daughters at all?

He had three daughters.

5. **Where did the three poor daughters hang their stockings?**

Did they hang them in the closet?

Did they hang them under the bed?

Did they hang them by the fireplace?

Did they hang them on their noses?

They hung their stockings by the fireplace.

6. What is a dowry?

   Is it a kind of toy?

   Is it a kind of animal?

   Is it a kind of fish?

   Is it money needed for a girl's wedding?

   It is money needed for a girl's wedding.

7. Where did Nicholas throw the bags of gold?

   Did he throw them through the window?

   Did he throw them in the garbage?

   Did he throw them out to sea?

   Did he throw them through the door?

   He threw them through the window.

8. At the end of the story, what did Nicholas become?

   Did he become president?

   Did he become a king?

   Did he become a monk?

   Did he become a saint?

   Nicholas became a saint.

9. The spirit of St. Nicholas is still alive today in which jolly old soul?

Is it Rudolph the Red-Nosed Reindeer?

Is it Frosty the Snowman?

Is it Jack Frost?

Is it Santa Claus?

Of course, the answer is Santa Claus.

10. On what night do children around the world hang their stockings by the fireplace?

Is it on New Year's Eve?

Is it on Christmas Eve?

Is it on Thanksgiving?

Is it on Halloween?

They hang up their stockings on Christmas Eve.

A Journey to Santa's Castle

I. **What color is Santa Claus's suit?**

Is it purple?

Is it pink?

Is it yellow?

Is it red?

It is red.

2. **What does Santa ride around the world in?**

Does he ride in a boat?

Does he ride on a bicycle?

Does he ride in a sleigh?

Does he ride in a rocket ship?

He rides in a sleigh.

3. What kind of children does Santa Claus like?

Does he like naughty children?

Does he like pouty children?

Does he like rude children?

Does he like nice children?

Santa Claus likes nice children.

4. When does Santa deliver presents?

Is it on Easter morning?

Is it on Halloween night?

Is it on New Year's Day?

Is it on Christmas Eve?

Santa delivers presents on Christmas Eve.

5. What do many children around the world send to Santa Claus?

Do they send flowers?

Do they send clothes?

Do they send pizza?

Do they send letters?

Children send letters to Santa Claus.

6. **What do reindeer grow on their heads?**

    Do they grow trees?

    Do they grow tomatoes?

    Do they grow hats?

    Do they grow antlers?

    Reindeer grow antlers on their heads.

7. **What color is Santa's beard?**

    Is it brown?

    Is it blue?

    Is it white?

    Is it black?

    Santa Claus has a white beard.

8. **What does Santa Claus say when he laughs?**

    Does he say "hee hee hee"?

    Does he say "ha ha ha"?

    Does he say "hi hi hi"?

    Does he say "ho ho ho"?

    Santa Claus says "ho ho ho" when he laughs.

9. **What does Santa Claus make in his workshop?**

Does he bake cakes?

Does he knit sweaters?

Does he make toys?

Does he write books?

Santa Claus makes toys in his workshop.

10. **What kind of animals pull Santa's sleigh?**

Are they moose?

Are they giraffes?

Are they elephants?

Are they reindeer?

Reindeer pull Santa's sleigh.

Selected Readings

*W*e list here the books and websites about Christmas and the sources of the traditional Christmas tales that we used in writing this book. In our retelling of the Nativity, we used the Gospels of St. Matthew and St. Luke in the King James Version of the Bible.

BOOKS

BOWLER, GERRY. *The World Encyclopedia of Christmas.* Toronto: McClelland & Stewart, 2000.

CRUMP, WILLIAM D. *The Christmas Encyclopedia.* Jefferson, NC: McFarland & Co., 2001.

DICKENS, CHARLES. *Christmas Books.* London: The Nonesuch Press, 1937. Barnes and Noble Books edition, 2005.

HOFFMANN, E.T.A. (Pictures by Maurice Sendak). *The Nutcracker.* New York: Gramercy Books, 1984.

WORLD BOOK ENCYCLOPEDIA. Chicago: World Book–Childcraft International, 1978.

WEBSITES

Bama Babies and Birthdays Celebration Sign Rentals. 2004. "The Stork Legend." <www.bamababiesandbirthdays.com/storklegend.htm>

WorldOfChristmas.net. 2005. "Legend of the Robin." <www.worldofchristmas.net/christmas-stories/legend-of-robin.html>

Jeff Westover. 1989–2005. "The Legends of Nature at the Nativity." The Merry Network. <www.mymerrychristmas.com/2005/nature.shtml>

St. Nicholas Center. 2002–2006. "Who Is St. Nicholas?" <www.stnicholascenter.org/Brix?pageID=38>

Send Us Your Christmas Trivia Questions

*I*n this book and our original Quizmas book we answer many questions about all aspects of Christmas. But there is so much belief, history, folklore, literature, and tradition associated with the holiday that you may still have some unanswered Christmas questions of your own. Or you may think of a question to which you already know the answer that you would like to share with others. In either case, send it to us. If you don't know the answer, we'll do our best to find it and post it on our Quizmas.net website. If you do know the correct response, give it to us and save us some work. Mail it to the address below or visit www.quizmas.net and use the special email form there. We'd be delighted to hear from you.

Quizmas
Suite 181
16715 – 12 Yonge Street
Newmarket, Ontario
Canada   L3X 1X4
www.quizmas.net

Acknowledgments

*T*his book could never have been written had it not been for the work of many great writers who, over centuries dating back to biblical times, have woven the many beautiful threads of the Christmas story into our cultural and religious fabric. In doing so, they expanded and enriched the traditions surrounding this most special time of the year and created legends and images that have become an integral part of our Christmas heritage.

A Christmas Carol, Charles Dickens's classic tale of the redemption of a doomed soul, resonates in our hearts as much today as when he first wrote it more than 150 years ago. E.T.A. Hoffmann's *The Nutcracker,* adapted by Peter Ilich Tchaikovsky into a magical ballet, has become part of Christmas for children from America to Russia. Clement Clarke Moore's "A Visit from St. Nicholas" (also known as "The Night Before Christmas") is read aloud on Christmas Eve in virtually every home where a young child hangs a Christmas stocking. These are only a few examples.

So we begin by acknowledging our debt of thanks to all those writers who have preceded us. St. Matthew and St. Luke chronicled the events surrounding the birth of Jesus and in doing so left the world a priceless legacy. The rich imaginations of

Dickens, Hoffmann, Moore, and others embellished the Christmas tradition and added new dimensions to our understanding and appreciation. All we have done in this book is to try to make their work more meaningful to a younger audience by retelling their stories in a form suitable for parents and grandparents to read aloud just before a small child drifts off to sleep.

Moving forward to the present day, we also want to thank all of those who contributed to bringing our work to life. They include our editors, Andrea Crozier in Toronto and David Cashion in New York; our production editor, Sandra Tooze; our copy editor, Marcia Miron de Gallego; and Ron Lightburn who drew the wonderful full-page illustrations you will find within these pages and on the cover.